131

# THE WANING MIDDLE AGES

AN EXHIBITION OF FRENCH AND
NETHERLANDISH ART FROM 1350 TO 1500
COMMEMORATING THE FIFTIETH
ANNIVERSARY OF THE PUBLICATION OF
*THE WANING OF THE MIDDLE AGES*
BY JOHAN HUIZINGA

*catalogue by*
J. L. Schrader

THE UNIVERSITY OF KANSAS MUSEUM OF ART
NOVEMBER 1 - DECEMBER 1, 1969

# LENDERS TO THE EXHIBITION

Mr. John Goelet
The Lehman Collection
Mr. Gordon Pfeiffer
Mr. and Mrs. Germain Seligman
Two anonymous lenders

Albright-Knox Art Gallery, Buffalo
Allen Memorial Art Museum, Oberlin College
Andrew Dickson White Museum of Art, Cornell University
The Art Galleries, University of California, Santa Barbara
The Art Institute of Chicago
The Art Museum, Princeton University
Boston Public Library
City Art Museum of St. Louis
The Cleveland Museum of Art
The Corcoran Gallery of Art, Washington, D.C.
Cranbrook Academy of Art
The Denver Art Museum
The Detroit Institute of Arts
Fine Arts Gallery of San Diego
Fogg Art Museum, Harvard University
Los Angeles County Museum of Art
The Metropolitan Museum of Art, New York
M. H. De Young Memorial Museum, San Francisco
Museum of Art, Rhode Island School of Design, Providence
National Gallery of Art (Rosenwald Collection), Washington, D.C.
Nelson Gallery—Atkins Museum, Kansas City, Mo.
The New York Public Library
Philadelphia Museum of Art
The Pierpont Morgan Library
Princeton University Library
Seattle Art Museum
Smith College Museum of Art
Wadsworth Atheneum, Hartford, Conn.
The Walters Art Gallery, Baltimore
Williams College Museum of Art, Williamstown, Mass.
Worcester Art Museum
Yale University Art Gallery
Yale University Library

French & Company, Inc., New York
Paul Drey Gallery, New York
Edward R. Lubin, Inc., New York
H. Shickman Gallery, New York
Victor D. Spark

# FOREWORD

Fifty years ago, in 1919, the first edition of Johan Huizinga's brilliant study *The Waning of the Middle Ages* was published in the Netherlands. Later editions in other languages followed, the first English edition appearing in 1924.

As the fame of Huizinga's study spread, his ideas stirred controversy. *The Waning of the Middle Ages* is an eloquent exposition of Huizinga's thesis that the fourteenth and fifteenth centuries in France and the Netherlands witnessed not so much the dawn of the Renaissance as the close of the medieval era. Although other scholars have taken issue with this thesis, the importance of *The Waning of the Middle Ages* cannot be denied. It stands as a landmark in the study of medieval history; an inspired effort to synthesize political, economic and social history with research into the literature, music and art of the period in order to create a panoramic view of "the world when it was half a thousand years younger."

This exhibition, commemorating the fiftieth anniversary of the publication of *The Waning of the Middle Ages,* is conceived both as a tribute to Huizinga and as an occasion to re-examine some of his concepts in the light of visual evidence provided by works of art of the period. In this respect the exhibition continues a tradition established some years ago at The University of Kansas Museum of Art. In 1960, the centenary of the publication of Burckhardt's *Die Cultur der Renaissance in Italien,* an exhibition was held and a catalogue published under the title, *Jacob Burckhardt and the Renaissance: 100 Years After.* In 1962 appeared *A Study in Yellow,* an exhibition of drawings by contributors to the turn-of-the-century British periodical, *The Yellow Book;* in 1965 came *Les Mardis: Stéphane Mallarmé and the Artists of his Circle;* in 1967, *The School for Scandal; Thomas Rowlandson's London: An Account of his Life & Times, & Especially his Depictions of the Theatre, Together with some Discussion of the Life and Works of Richard Brinsley Sheridan & of His Play* The School for Scandal. . . . The present exhibition follows the same general pattern in bringing together works of art related to an important theme in the cultural history of a particular period.

Mr. J. L. Schrader, who has organized the exhibition and written the catalogue, joins me in thanking the lenders listed on the following page and the many individuals who have cooperated to make this exhibition possible. Miss Dorothy Miner, Librarian and Keeper of Manuscripts at the Walters Art Gallery, has been extraordinarily helpful, giving both encouragement and advice. The more than generous assistance of Dr. George Szabo, Curator of the Lehman Collection, also deserves our particular thanks. In addition to participating as a lender Mr. Edward R. Lubin has kindly directed our attention to several important works which otherwise we might not have located. Mrs. Ruth Ziser, a student in the Department of History of Art at The University of Kansas, assisted in the preliminary research for this exhibition. Her work was supported by an Undergraduate Research Grant from the College of Arts and Sciences, The University of Kansas.

We wish to acknowledge our indebtedness to the late Mr. Robert Lehman and express our gratitude to Mr. Lessing J. Rosenwald, Mr. John Goelet, Mr. Gordon Pfeiffer, Mr. and Mrs. Germain Seligman, Mrs. Elizabeth M. Drey, Mr. Victor Spark, Mr. Norman Leitman, Mr. Kenneth L. Beech, and to two anonymous private lenders.

Our special thanks go also to Mr. Charles E. Buckley, City Art Museum of St. Louis; Mr. Walter Zervas, The New York Public Library; Dr. Sherman E. Lee and Mr. William Wixom, The Cleveland Museum of Art; Mr. Willis F. Woods and Mr. Francis Robinson, The Detroit Institute of Arts; Mr. D. Graeme Keith, M. H. De Young Memorial Museum; Mr. Andrew C. Ritchie, Yale University Art Gallery; Mr. Herman W. Liebert, Yale University Library; Mr. Gordon M. Smith, Albright-Knox Gallery; Mr. James Harithas, The Corcoran Gallery of Art; Mr. David W. Heron and Miss Alexandra Mason, University of Kansas Libraries; Mr. Laurence Sickman and Mr. Ralph T. Coe, Nelson Gallery of Art and Atkins Museum; Dr. Thomas P. F. Hoving, Dr. Florens Deuchler, Dr. William H. Forsyth, Mr. Thomas P. Miller, Miss Vera K. Ostoia, Dr. Helmut Nickel and Mr. John J. McKendry, The Metropolitan Museum of Art; Mr. Charles C. Cunningham, Dr. John Maxon and Mr. Harold Joachim, The Art Institute of Chicago; Mr. Howard C. Rice, Jr., Princeton University Library; Mr. Patrick J. Kelleher and Miss Frances Follin Jones, The Art Museum, Princeton University; Dr. Richard E. Fuller, Seattle Art Museum; Mr. Charles H. Sawyer, The Museum of Art, University of Michigan; Mr. Wallace Mitchell, Cranbrook Academy of Art; Mr. Daniel Catton Rich and Mr. John David Farmer, Worcester Art Museum; Mr. Thomas W. Leavitt, Andrew Dickson White Museum of Art, Cornell University; Mr. James W. Lawton, Boston Public Library; Mr. Herbert Cahoon, The Pierpont Morgan Library; Mr. S. Lane Faison, Jr., Williams College Museum of Art; Dr. Otto Karl Bach, The Denver Art Museum; Dr. Richard H. Randall, Jr., The Walters Art Gallery; Miss Agnes Mongan, Fogg Art Museum, Harvard University; Dr. Hanns Swarzenski and Miss Pamela Tosi, Museum of Fine Arts, Boston; Mr. Charles Chetham and Mr. Michael Wentworth, Smith College Museum of Art; Mr. David Gebhard, The Art Galleries, University of California, Santa Barbara; Mr. Kenneth Donahue, Los Angeles County Museum of Art; Mr. John R. Spencer and Mrs. Chloe H. Young, Allen Memorial Art Museum, Oberlin College; Mr. Warren Beach, Fine Arts Gallery of San Diego; Mr. Peter O. Marlow, Wadsworth Atheneum; Dr. Evan H. Turner and Mr. David DuBon, Philadelphia Museum of Art; Mr. Fred Cain, Alverthorpe Gallery; Mr. Addison Franklin Page, The J. B. Speed Art Museum; Mr. Daniel J. Robbins and Dr. Stephen E. Ostrow, Museum of Art, Rhode Island School of Design.

BRET WALLER
*Director*

# CATALOGUE

## MANUSCRIPTS AND SINGLE MINIATURES

### 1  PARIS, 1336

Guilielmus Durandus, *In sententias Petri Lombardi*

Ms. in Latin: Vol. I of 2 vols., 199 vellum leaves in Gothic script with 2 historiated initials and illuminated borders, H. 16-1/16 inches (40.7 cm.), W. 11-3/16 inches (28.5 cm.)

This manuscript is related to the workshop of Jean Pucelle, the famous illuminator in the employ of Charles IV of France, as was first pointed out by A. E. Bye. In discussing the similarity of the border decoration to that in Pucelle's finest work, the *Belleville Breviary* (Paris, Bibliothèque Nationale, mss. lat., 10483-4), written between the years 1323-1326 for Jeanne de Belleville, Bye pointed out that in the marginal drolleries there are exact duplications of some of the patterns used in Pucelle's manuscript. The "pucelle," or dragonfly, which is used in the ornament, copies the motif that is usually thought to have been used intentionally by Pucelle as a rebus signature. However, Bye's hypothesis that the present manuscript was illuminated not by Pucelle or his workshop, but by another Parisian atelier with access to some of the Pucelle models, is generally accepted. The manuscript was written in Paris in 1336 for Simon Comitis of Naples by the English scribe, William of Kirkby-in-Lincolnshire. The didactic Durandus text would be an appropriate addition to the library of a member of the Dominican order, whose chapter in Paris Comitis headed.

The illuminated initial on fol. 1 recto shows Durandus wearing his bishop's mitre, teaching a group seated beneath the image of an enthroned Virgin and Child. The arrangement with the boy standing at the head of the class is reminiscent of the principal miniature in the famous English *Apocalypse* of Trinity College, Cambridge, of a hundred years before, in which a musician plays before the banquet table of the Holy Lamb. Indeed, there was much exchange between England and France at the time, but the English influence is more prominent in the *bas-de-page,* or lower marginal strip of illustration often of a secular nature (here a stag hunt), which is developed for its own sake. It is the triumph of French synthesis that gives the page, with its drolleries in the margins and the *rinceaux* dividing it into two columns, its unified character. Otherwise, the figures and architectural interest derive ultimately from Italian models, while the harvest of naturalistic motifs is reaped from more northern territory. Panofsky has described the manuscript as being entirely removed from the wave of Italianism with which the style of Pucelle was infused around the time of the *Belleville Breviary*. Dorothy Miner has called attention to the artist's failure to grasp the essence of Pucelle's fluid and graceful style in spite of his assimilation of Pucelle's motifs and organization. The directness of observation is absent, as are Pucelle's subtleties of modelling and his "aristocratic decorative charm."

EX COLLECTION: Earl of Ashburnham (Appendix no. 253); H. Yates Thompson (Sale, London, May 11, 1901, no. 16); Robert Garrett, Baltimore.

EXHIBITIONS: Baltimore Museum of Art, "Illuminated Books of the Middle Ages and Renaissance," 1949, no. 69.

REFERENCES: A. E. Bye, in *Art in America*, IV, 1916, pp. 98-118, figs. 1-3; De Ricci and Wilson, *Census*, I, p. 880, no. 83; Donald D. Egbert, in Princeton University Library *Chronicle*, III, 1942, p. 127, ill.; [Dorothy Miner], *Illuminated Books of the Middle Ages and Renaissance* (exhibition catalogue), Baltimore, 1949, pp. 27-28, no. 69; Erwin Panofsky, *Early Netherlandish Painting*, Cambridge, Mass., 1953, pp. 42, 34, n. 32 (4); Princeton University Library *Chronicle*, XXVII, 3, 1966, p. 187, no. 15.

PLATE II

Lent by Princeton University Library,
Princeton, New Jersey, Garrett ms. 83

2   FRANCE, 1357

Robert de Borron, *Le Roman du Saint Gral; Le Roman de Merlin*

Ms. in French: 316 vellum leaves in Gothic script in 3 cols. with 2 large and 162 small miniatures, decorative and historiated initials, H. 16-1/2 inches (41.9 cm.), W. 11-15/16 inches (30.4 cm.)

For the Later Middle Ages King Arthur stood as the greatest example of chivalry and heroism. In Jacques de Longuyon's *Les Voeux du Paon,* he is one of the *neuf preux* or "nine worthies," which tradition is carried on in the poetry of Guillaume de Machaut and his pupil, Eustache Deschamps, and finds its finest visual expression in the set of *Heroes Tapestries,* probably woven for the Duc de Berry in the workshop of Nicholas Bataille in Paris during the last quarter of the fourteenth century (Metropolitan Museum of Art, New York). When an early fifteenth-century transcriber of the *Roman de Brut* named Jean Vaillent de Poitiers writes in his transcription of an Arthurian text about the history of his book, he feels obliged to mention those of his predecessors who have treated the Arthurian legends, including Luce du Gast, Gasse le Blond, Robert de Borron, Helie de Borron and Walter Map. The present text is that by Robert de Borron which Vaillent mentions. It is written in a fine, bold Gothic hand, which we are told by the colophon is that of a Fleming, Johan de Loles of Hainault, who finished the writing on the first Saturday of July, 1357. The manuscript contains a very large number of miniatures and provides a blank for one that was never executed. Under these, including the one that was never painted, there are written instructions to aid the artist in painting the scenes to be represented. The romance is told in the miniatures in a very fresh and lively style. The figures are endowed with movement and placed in settings with buildings and landscape devices. In many instances the instructions to the artist were cut away after he had finished the miniatures, but mostly they have been left for us to compare the contents of the instructions and the miniatures.

EX COLLECTION: The family of Clermont-Tonnèrre; Yarnold: Evans sale, May 27, 1825; Sir Thomas Phillipps, Middle Hill, Worcestershire and Thirlestaine House, Cheltenham, ms. 1045; W. H. Robinson; D. M. Colman; [Stonehill].

REFERENCES: Sale catalogue of the Sir Thomas Phillipps Collection at Sotheby's, London, July 1, 1946, no. 14; Yale University Library *Gazette*, XXIX, 1955, pp. 104-105, 110; W. H. Bond and C. U. Faye, Supplement to the *Census of Medieval and Renaissance Manuscripts in the United States and Canada*, New York, 1962, p. 43, no. 227.

Lent by Yale University Library,
New Haven, Connecticut

PLATE III

3   FRANCE, late 14th century

Guillaume de Tignonville, *Dits des Philosophes;* Apollonius of Tyre, *Le miroir aux pecheurs:* Un roi fu jadis appelle antioche x et laisse l'autre en sa libraire; *Le Livre Griseldis ou l'exemplaire des femmes; Miroir des pecheurs*

Ms. in French: 101 vellum leaves with 24 miniatures in *grisaille*, H. 12-3/16 inches (31.0 cm.), W. 9-7/16 inches (24.0 cm.)

This *grisaille*-illuminated manuscript, probably written at the end of the four-teenth century during the reign of Charles VI, includes several popular late Medieval texts that have moral overtones, the principal of which is the first by Guillaume de Tignonville. It is not a luxury production, as evidenced by the uneven bâtarde script and the somewhat hastily rendered *rinceaux*. The minia-tures betray the linearism of the Pucelle revival in Paris during the reign of Charles V; nevertheless, they strive for an elegance that is characteristic of the later period. The quilt-like background pattern of the miniatures is virtually a trademark of many Parisian ateliers at the end of the century, and the figure receiving the book on fol. 1 recto is up-to-date in fashionable clothing typical of the period of the International Style.

EX COLLECTION: [A. Rosenthal, New York].

REFERENCES: Margaret Munsterberg, in *More Books*, XVI, 1941, pp. 315-321; W. H. Bond and C. U. Faye, Supplement to the *Census of Medieval and Renaissance Manuscripts in the United States and Canada*, New York, 1962, p. 209, no. 91.

PLATE IX　　　　　　　　　　　　　　Lent by The Boston Public Library, ms. 1518

4　BRUGES, ca. 1385-1390

*The Crucifixion: single leaf from a Missal*

Tempera and gold leaf on parchment, H. 10-3/4 inches (27.3 cm.), W. 8 inches (20.3 cm.)

The series of tapestries designed by Jean Bondol for Louis I, Duke of Anjou, and known as the *Angers Apocalypse,* the miniatures attributed to Jacquemart de Hesdin in the *Très Belles Heures* of the Duc de Berry, and other courtly produc-tion in France during the last quarter of the fourteenth century, demand partial explanation in the art of Flanders and other regions to the north of France. The Netherlands was rich in artistic talent, and the willingness with which immigrant artists were accepted in France is demonstrated by an entire generation of leading Franco-Flemish artists. Of the great painters in France during the reign of Charles V and the early reign of Charles VI, Jean Bondol had been born in Bruges, Jacquemart de Hesdin hailed from the region incorporated with Flanders and known as the Artois, and Jean Malouel had brought his baggage from Guelders.

　This "Crucifixion" miniature, the frontispiece for the Canon of the Mass in a Missal, was produced around the same time as Jacquemart de Hesdin's *Très Belles Heures,* but in the North, probably at Bruges. The regional connections with the emigrated artist working in Paris are strong, but they are limited to the homespun realism and a softness in the modelling. The style is characterized by much fine pen-drawing that enlivens the surfaces, and by a penchant for realistic detail. The binding on St. John's book, for example, and the details of costume of the soldier and of the man at the far left are indications of the artist's realistic awareness. An innate sense for the pictorial held together by symbolism raises this miniature to a level of utter sophistication. The tilted tablet nailed to the top of the cross appears haphazard before it is interpreted together with the sun and the moon, symbols of the believer and the unbeliever; then it reads like the scale of St. Michael in the Last Judgment. The sinister laughing expression of Adam's skull tempers the meek and introverted sorrow of St. John, and steals some of the attention from the soldier's marked gesture toward Christ. In spite of the solid backdrop there is spatial interest, especially at the sides where the ground rises behind the figures. Here the decorative frame arbitrarily cuts off an imaginary space, so that the scene is interpreted as being viewed through a window.

As in the Missal in the Museum Meermanno-Westreenianum in the Hague (ms. 10 A 14), produced in Ghent, not far from Bruges, in 1366, the interest in realistic qualities and in space is outspokenly Flemish. The artist of our miniature is the inheritor of a tradition that Jean Bondol partly transplanted, but did not remove, to France. It is in the artist's reluctance to idealize the face of Christ that we see the absence of contact with the French courtly style and more the relationships with contemporary England.

EXHIBITIONS: Cincinnati, Ohio, Taft Museum, "Medieval Art Exhibition from the XIIth to the XVth Centuries," 1948-1949; Oberlin, Ohio, Allen Memorial Art Museum, "An Exhibition of Netherlandish Illumination," 1960, no. 3; Berkeley, University of California, University Art Gallery, "Medieval and Renaissance Illuminated Manuscripts from the Xth to the Early XVIth Centuries," 1963, no. 21; Cleveland Museum of Art, "Gothic Art 1360-1440," 1963, no. 9.

REFERENCES: William M. Milliken, in Cleveland Museum of Art *Bulletin*, XII, 1925, p. 77, ill. pp. 70-71; De Ricci and Wilson, *Census*, II, p. 1930; Harry Bober, in *Miscellanea Prof. D. Roggen*, Antwerp, 1957, pp. 35-45, fig. 1; *An Exhibition of Netherlandish Illumination* (exhibition catalogue), Oberlin, 1960, no. 3; *Medieval and Renaissance Illuminated Manuscripts from the Xth to the Early XVIth Centuries* (exhibition catalogue), Berkeley, 1963, no. 21, ill.; *Gothic Art 1360-1440* (exhibition catalogue), Cleveland, 1963, no. 9, ill.; William D. Wixom, in Cleveland Museum of Art *Bulletin*, LII, 1965, p. 83, n. 58.

Lent by The Cleveland Museum of Art,
PLATE X                                          Gift of J. H. Wade, 24.1014

5   PARIS (atelier of Jacquemart de Hesdin), ca. 1400

*The Nativity: single miniature from a Book of Hours*

Tempera on vellum, H. 3-15/16 inches (10.0 cm.), W. 2-3/16 inches (7.2 cm.), without present frame

This small, exquisitely painted miniature belongs to a set of illuminations known as the Ranshaw miniatures, of which four others are now in the Museum of Fine Arts in Boston.

The miniatures illustrated the Hours of the Virgin and of the Cross in a Book of *Hours* now lost. Rosy Schilling has rightly attributed the miniatures to the workshop of Jacquemart de Hesdin, the author of the illuminations in three luxury manuscripts commissioned and prized by the celebrated Duc de Berry: the *Très Belles Heures* (Brussels, Bibliothèque Royale, mss. 11060-61), and the *Grandes Heures* and *Petites Heures* (Paris, Bibliothèque Nationale, lat. 919 and 18014, respectively). Jacquemart, whose known activity spans the years 1384-1409, was one of the Duke's favorite illuminators. As one of the primary innovators of the International Style he helped foster the new realism so indicative of the course fifteenth-century art was to take.

Here in the "Nativity" attention is centered on the quaint St. Joseph and on the humble aspects of the setting—the thatched roof, woven fence, and wooden tub—all of this placed before a checkered background. That the artist is not quite so careful as the master of the workshop is shown by the way he allows lines to cross into objects behind which they are supposed to run. But it is partly in the sketchiness of such details as the roof that this miniature holds its special charm.

The scene in this miniature for illustrating part of the Hours of the Virgin is actually the ceremony of washing the newborn Child. The midwife performs the ablutions while Joseph waits eagerly with a towel to receive the Child. Among

10

the most charming details are the straw strewn on the floor and the decorative belt worn by the midwife.

EX COLLECTION: Miss E. M. Ranshaw (Sale, London, Sotheby's, 1943).

REFERENCES: Rosy Schilling in *Burlington Magazine*, LXXXIV, 1944, p. 20; Georg Swarzenski, in *Bulletin of the Museum of Fine Arts*, Boston, 1944, XLII, p. 28; *The Gothic Room, Los Angeles County Museum* (catalogue), p. 12, fig. 16; W. R. Valentiner, in *Bulletin of the Art Museum, Los Angeles County Museum*, Summer, 1950, p. 19; *Catalogue of Paintings, Los Angeles County Museum*, I, 1954, p. 57, pl. 55.

PLATE XII

Lent by The Los Angeles County Museum of Art, 47.19.1

6   PARIS (atelier or follower of the Boucicaut Master), ca. 1415-1420

*The Pentecost: single miniature from a pendant medallion reliquary*

Tempera on vellum, with crystal cover, Diam. 3 inches (7.6 cm.)

This is a truly exceptional miniature, for it was undoubtedly produced with the explicit purpose of decorating the reverse of a relief medallion of hardened polychromed wax to form a medallion with a reliquary. That it was not cut out of a manuscript is evidenced by the way in which the artist has carefully adjusted the composition to the circular format which matches the shape of the wax medallion used for the obverse. The wax relief representing the "Last Judgment" survived intact with the miniature until 1935. Both were held in an elaborate silver-gilt frame with a hanging device and polished crystal discs covering both sides of the pendant. In 1935 a thief broke into the glass case where the pendant was displayed and took with him all but the "Pentecost" miniature and its protective crystal. That the thief, presumably interested in the frame alone, should also have taken and probably destroyed the wax relief is extremely unfortunate, for Erwin Panofsky was later able to show that the relief was probably an early fifteenth-century Parisian goldsmith's model. For one reason or another its design never had been transformed into enamel-covered gold in the goldsmith's workshop and the model was saved and mounted as a pendant together with the "Pentecost" miniature that was made for the reverse at the time of the mounting. Such use of a goldsmith's wax model for a reliquary is in itself unusual. The special production of a miniature to decorate such an object, however, is virtually unparalleled in contemporary illumination.

Panofsky also noted that the miniature is in the style of the Master of the *Hours* of Jean Le Meingre, the Maréchal de Boucicaut (Paris, Musée Jacquemart-André, ms. 2), and that it must have been executed by a close associate of the Boucicaut Master. He was able to relate it stylistically to Pentecost miniatures from the Boucicaut Master workshop in the two *Hours* in the Bibliothèque Mazarine in Paris (ms. 469, fol. 117) and the Walters Art Gallery in Baltimore (ms. 260, fol. 123), pointing out that the artist's treatment of the hair and the Virgin's halo shows his slight leaning toward the style of the contemporary and closely related workshop of the Master of the *Hours of Rohan*. Iconographically, however, the miniature would represent an extraordinary departure from the usual representation of the Pentecost because it breaks all tradition by granting St. James the Great the privilege of wearing his pilgrim's hat with cockle shell, his usual attribute, on this occasion. Panofsky concluded that St. James had a special meaning for the person who ordered the miniature and mounting for the wax relief and that the reliquary medallion may have been assembled as an *ex voto* in commemoration of a pilgrimage to Santiago de Compostela.

11

The Boucicaut Master was a great articulator when it came to adapting the conventions of late fourteenth-century Parisian illuminators to the pictorial and technical improvements of which he was a primary instigator during the early fifteenth century. Besides his innovative interpretation of space, his concern for vital qualities and realistic detail mark him as one of the great personalities of pre-Eyckian painting. The cogency of his style is felt as well in the many surviving products of his atelier and followers. Here in the ingenious asymmetrical composition of the "Pentecost," the artist is careful not to remove St. Peter from his traditional central position, and in fact leads the spectator's eye back to him by means of a row of Apostles at the left. At the same time, the Virgin is given a place of prominence between two seated Apostles slightly to the right of center, while in the background a youthful, unbearded Apostle establishes visual contact with the dove that descends from above a row of naturalistic clouds.

EX COLLECTION: Albin Chalandon, Lyon; Georges Chalandon, Paris.

EXHIBITIONS: Detroit Institute of Arts, "French Gothic Art of the Thirteenth to Fifteenth Century," 1928, no. 18.

REFERENCES: [W. R. Valentiner], *French Gothic Art of the Thirteenth to Fifteenth Century* (exhibition catalogue), Detroit, 1928, no. 18 (as "Burgundian school, about 1430"); *Bulletin of the Detroit Institute of Arts,* IX, 1928, p. 60; Erwin Panofsky, in *Essays in Honor of Georg Swarzenski,* Berlin, 1951, pp. 70-84.

PLATE XII

Lent by The Detroit Institute of Arts,
Gift of Mrs. James Couzins Fund, 27.162

7   GHENT, ca. 1420-1425

*Book of Hours for use of Arras*

Ms. in Latin and Flemish: 186 vellum leaves in Gothic script, with 13 full-page miniatures, historiated initials, drolleries and illuminated borders, H. 6-1/4 inches (16.0 cm.), W. 4-5/8 inches (11.2 cm.)

This Book of *Hours* was made for the private devotional use of a prominent patrician of the city of Ghent, Daniel Rym, and his wife, Elizabeth van Munte. The armorial bearings of the two are included in the border decoration, and on fol. 168 verso, outside of the rosette frame of the miniature with "Daniel in the Lion's Den," Daniel Rym (d. 1431) is shown kneeling on a turf of grass, the words of his veneration for his patron saint written on a scroll which issues from between his praying hands. The *Hours of Daniel Rym,* the *Hours of John the Fearless* (Bibliothèque Nationale, ms. nouv. acq. lat. 3055), and another Book of *Hours* in The Walters Art Gallery (ms. W. 170), are all closely interrelated productions of an early school of Ghent illumination which Panofsky has characterized as partly growing out of a Guelders-related Ypres tradition and as exhibiting some traits that are again apparent in the later workshop of the anonymous Master of Gilbert of Metz.

Leroquais was the first to connect the *Hours of Daniel Rym* with the slightly earlier Book of *Hours* made for John the Fearless (d. 1419), which unfortunately does not preserve its donor page. According to Panofsky, the latter is the earliest of the group immediately concerned, while several miniatures inserted into a later manuscript now in the Royal Library in The Hague (ms. 131 G 3) already around 1400 show some of the earmarks of the Ghent style. The borders of our manuscript present an array of somewhat archaic, but graceful, undulating *rinceaux* of French inspiration, interspersed with elaborate floral motifs that often spread to the corners of the page. Dorothy Miner (1962, p. 72) has pointed to the presence of similar floral decoration on a previously unpublished single leaf in the Louis Collection of the Philadelphia Free Library. On some pages of the *Hours of Daniel Rym,* as on the page with the "Betrayal of Christ" miniature, the flowers have a tendency to break across the frame of the miniature, and likewise the miniatures overstep the bounds of the frame. The simple palmette-shaped leaves in the *rinceaux* are fewer than those shaped somewhat like oak leaves, and now and again a spiked lozenge of gold makes its appearance. Like other manuscripts of the group, this one reveals English connections. These in turn are related back to the Continent because many continental artists, among them the illuminator now identified with Herman Scheere, worked in England.

The Ypres relationship is strongly manifest on the page with the "Virgin and Child in Glory" miniature, for here flying angels appear in the border grasping tendrils of the *rinceaux.* Panofsky has called attention, too, to the fact that our Book of *Hours* shows the same use as an Ypres school Book of *Hours,* now the property of the Clowes Foundation in Indianapolis. Though the Virgin's face in the miniature representing "The Virgin and Child in Glory" has been described as "vacuous," this miniature shows knowledge of the work of Jacquemart de Hesdin and the Parisian ateliers, especially of the *Très Belles Heures* of the Duc de Berry. A note of iconographic subtlety in this miniature is the Virgin's gown of peacock feathers, which is almost completely hidden by her ample cloak. It serves to identify her with the all-seeing Holy Church. Some of the miniatures with narrative scenes exhibit leanings toward the fashionable Parisian ateliers and hold the surprise of a naturalistic sky in the manner of the Boucicaut Master; others depend on the local raw material of expressionism and, as Panofsky calls it, a "surprisingly subtle interpretation of serious subjects."

The end phase of the workshop which produced the *Hours of Daniel Rym* and the *Hours of John the Fearless* is represented by a Book of *Hours* in the John Carter Brown Library in Providence (ms. 3), dated ca. 1430-1435 by Panofsky. After this time the production in the area of Ghent moves to the large atelier of the Master of Gilbert of Metz, whose hand Delaissé claims is already present in the *Hours of John the Fearless* (reported by Dorothy Miner, 1960, p. 377). The present manuscript therefore holds a key position between developments around 1400 in the Netherlandish schools of book illumination and those of the second quarter of the fifteenth century.

EX COLLECTION: Made for Elizabeth van Munte and Daniel Rym (d. 1431), Ghent.

EXHIBITIONS: Baltimore Museum of Art, "Illuminated Books of the Middle Ages and Renaissance," 1949, no. 125; Los Angeles County Museum, "Medieval and Renaissance Illuminated Manuscripts," 1953-1954, no. 53; Oberlin, Ohio, Allen Memorial Art Museum, "Early Netherlandish Book Illumination," 1960, no. 26; Detroit Institute of Arts, "Masterpieces of Flemish Art: Van Eyck to Bosch," 1960, no. 197.

REFERENCES: De Ricci and Wilson, *Census,* I, p. 787, no. 190; V. Leroquais, *Un Livre d'Heures de Jean sans Peur,* Paris, 1939, p. 63 (erroneously referred to as W. 170); A. W. Byvanck, in *Oudheidkundig Jaarboek,* ser. iv, IX, 1940, p. 32, figs. 1, 2 (again referred to as W. 170 in error); [Dorothy Miner], *Illuminated Books of the Middle Ages and Renaissance* (exhibition catalogue), Baltimore, 1949, p. 47, no. 125; Millard Meiss, *Painting in Florence and Siena after the Black Death,* Princeton, 1951, p. 143, n. 47; *Medieval and Renaissance Illuminated Manuscripts* (exhibition catalogue), Los Angeles, 1953-1954, no. 74; Erwin Panofsky, *Early Netherlandish Painting,* Cambridge, Mass., 1953, pp. 119-121, notes 114 (6), 118 (8), 119 (2, 6, 8), 120 (5), 121 (1, 2, 6), figs. 186-189; David Diringer, *The Illuminated Book,* Cambridge, 1958, p. 440, pl. VII-29; Allen Memorial Art Museum *Bulletin,* XVII, 1960, p. 108, no. 26, fig. 9; [Dorothy Miner], in *Flanders in the Fifteenth Century: Art and Civilization* (exhibition catalogue), Detroit, 1960, pp. 377-379, no. 197, ill.; [*idem*], in *The International Style* (exhibition catalogue), Baltimore, 1962, pp. 72-73, no. 70, pl. XVII.

**PLATE XVI**

Lent by The Walters Art Gallery,<br>Baltimore, ms. W. 166

8  PARIS  (follower of the Bedford Master), ca. 1435-1440

Christine de Pisan, *Le Livre des trois vertus*

Ms. in French: 98 vellum leaves in bâtarde script with 1 miniature, H. 11-1/2 inches (29.0 cm), W. 7-3/4 inches (19.0 cm.)

This is the text of one of the famous prose works of Christine de Pisan, who, like a literary Joan of Arc, fought for France with her pen. Although she challenged some of the great men of France and presented some of her works in admiration to others, including Philip the Good of Burgundy, and Jean, Duc de Berry, her principal concern was for the position held by women in society during her time. In one of her works she lauded with praise a certain woman artist named Anastaise, whom she had permitted to illustrate her manuscript writings.

Needless to say, it would be hopeless to look for the hand of Anastaise in the miniatures of surviving illustrated manuscript versions of Christine's works. The present one was probably written in Paris and provided with its single miniature by a follower of the Master who illuminated the *Hours* of John of Lancaster, Duke of Bedford (London, British Museum, Add. Ms. 18850), and who was active during the second and third decades of the fifteenth century. The Bedford style is notable for its vivid colors and lively compositions. The half-page miniature depicts at the left the Three Virtues appearing to Christine in a vision; at the right a group of ladies is being taught in the school of these Virtues. Several fifteenth-century manuscript versions of the text are known, including ones in the Bibliothèque Nationale in Paris and one with three handsome half-page miniatures recently acquired in this country. Charity Willard suggested a date of ca. 1450 for the present manuscript, which seems too late for the style of the miniature. She is inclined to connect the inscription written at the end of the book referring to its ownership by a certain "Monseigneur de Saint-Vallier" with Jean de Poitiers, Seigneur de Saint-Vallier, the father of Diane de Poitiers. She further speculates that Diane may have inherited the manuscript from her father and kept it in her famous library.

EX COLLECTION:  Jean de Poitiers (?); N. Yemeniz (Sale, Paris, 1867, lot 536); [Leclerc, Paris]; Erwin Rosenthal, 1919.

REFERENCES:  Charity C. Willard, in Boston Public Library *Quarterly,* II, 1950, pp. 291-305; W. H. Bond and C. U. Faye, Supplement to the *Census of Medieval and Renaissance Manuscripts in the United States and Canada,* New York, 1962, pp. 210-211, no. 101.

**PLATE XVI**                    Lent by The Boston Public Library, ms. 1528

9  NORTHERN FRANCE, ca. 1460

*Saint Catherine: single leaf from a Book of Hours*

Tempera on vellum, H. 9-1/16 inches (23.0 cm.), W. 6-11/16 inches (17.0 cm.)

Saint Catherine of Alexandria is shown trampling the Emperor Maximian in the miniature on this page from the suffrages of a Book of *Hours.* The miniature shows a predilection for surface decorative effects in the garments and the uncommon use of black. The circular canopy and tessellated background are holdovers from an earlier period, while the complicated patterns of drapery are characteristic of the second half of the fifteenth century. The manuscript from which this leaf came, written in Gothic script, was probably produced in one of the ateliers in northern France.

EX COLLECTION: Kalebdjian.

REFERENCES: H. Comstock, in *International Studio*, April, 1927, p. 47, ill.; De Ricci and Wilson, *Census*, II, no. 1711.

PLATE LII                                      Lent by The Lehman Collection, New York

10    FRANCE, ca. 1450

Gilles de Rome, *Livre du gouvernement des rois et des princes et des secrets d'Aristote;* Jacques Le Grand, *Sophologe*

Ms. in French: 85 vellum leaves in bâtarde script with 2 miniatures, H. 12-11/16 inches (29.7 cm.), W. 8-1/4 inches (21.5 cm.)

The main text, like that composed for Louis, the son of Philip the Bold (known best in the translation by Jean Golein for Charles V as *L'Information des rois et des princes*), examines the various qualities that a king should possess in order to be a good ruler. The small miniature on fol. 2 recto shows a kneeling figure presenting a book to the French king. The more elaborate miniature on fol. 25 recto marks the beginning of the chapter called the *"Remède contre les sept pechez mortels."* Shown in the latter is the ermine-robed king, behind whom stand a pair of his soldiers and other secular representatives of his court, while opposite stands a bishop, other ecclesiastical representatives, and representatives of both the middle and lower classes of society. It is interesting that the artist, in moving from the peasants at the far left toward the bishop in the center, lets his style become progressively more austere. The Christ of the Last Judgment, with the Virgin Mary and St. John the Baptist as intercessors, appears above the king and bishop who are shown in lively discussion.

Although it is difficult to localize this manuscript with any certainty, it most assuredly documents the shift in production away from Paris and into other parts of France about mid-century. Yet it seems not to be connected with Tours or any of the centers in the Loire Valley or Burgundy; rather, perhaps, with one of the centers in the North, like Lille, that were near the border of Flanders and produced manuscripts for the court of Burgundy in Flanders. There is a great similarity between the figures of this manuscript, especially the head types and eyes, and those in the miniatures of a Cicero manuscript in the Bibliothèque Royale in Brussels (cf. [L. M. J. Delaissé], *La Miniature Flamande. Le Mécénat de Philippe le Bon* [exhibition catalogue], Brussels, 1959, no. 21). Delaissé (1959, p. 17) has made a grouping of essentially Flemish manuscripts of which the miniatures are similar to ones executed in northern France during the same period. The coat-of-arms at the bottom of fol. 25 of the present manuscript has not been interpreted.

EX COLLECTION: [D. Morgand, Paris]; Robert Garrett, Baltimore.

REFERENCES: *Livres et manuscrits* (catalogue of the dealer D. Morgand), Paris, 1900, nos. 4-5; De Ricci and Wilson, *Census*, I, p. 891.

PLATES XXX, XXXI                    Lent by Princeton University Library, Princeton, New Jersey, Garrett ms. 130

11　HESDIN (Loyset Liédet atelier and the Master of Edward IV), ca. 1455-1460

Jean Mansel, *La Fleur des Histoires,* Vol. II

Ms. in French: 310 vellum leaves in bâtarde script with 2 large and 2 small miniatures, H. 18 inches (46.0 cm.), W. 13-1/2 inches (34.0 cm.)

From about 1445 onward manuscript illumination in Flanders shows a rapid growth and development. A major shift of artistic interest to Flanders had occurred when Philip the Bold, who had acceded to the throne of Burgundy when Duke John the Fearless was murdered in 1419, moved the Burgundian court to Flanders. In 1437 Philip acquired the Hainault and unified the northern territories, making them into the powerful and wealthy state that was to become an ever increasing threat to the interests of the King of France. Philip's patronage of the arts was unmitigatedly pursued in Flanders. Among other things he was a great bibliophile, and some of the manuscript ateliers that sprang up contributed almost exclusively to the shelves of his library. The manuscript copy of *La Fleur des Histoires* of Jean Mansel, of which volume II is shown here (a volume III also from the Liédet atelier, but apparently made for a different set, is preserved in the Bibliothèque Royale in Brussels, ms. 9233) was produced for Philip in the atelier of Loyset Liédet in Hesdin. Liédet was the chief miniaturist in a workshop in Hesdin which was supervised by an unidentified editor. Both the editions and the style of the illustrations at Hesdin show dependency on the atelier at Valenciennes, whose editor and translator was the author of this text, Jean Mansel, and one of whose principal miniaturists was the exceptionally gifted Simon Marmion. Delaissé has remarked on Marmion's strong influence in both of the large miniatures in this manuscript, one of which can be ascribed to the anonymous artist known as the Master of Edward IV (later active in Bruges), so-called because he executed the miniatures in several manuscripts produced for the English king. The large miniature on fol. 104, depicting "The Princes of the World Proceeding to the Court of the Emperor in Constantinople," is closest in style to the works of Liédet and has often been attributed to this head artist of the workshop. Liédet seems to have been first apprenticed to Simon Marmion at Valenciennes. Delaissé noticed that the script in this manuscript resembles that in the *Histoires romaines* from the Liédet workshop (Paris, Bibliothèque de l'Arsenal, mss. 5087-5088), for which the transcription was completed in 1455 and the payment made in 1460, and was the first to discover that the arms of the owner which had been cut out of the manuscript but had left take-offs on opposite pages were those of Philip the Good of Burgundy.

EX COLLECTION: Philip the Good, Duke of Burgundy; family of de Plaines (?); [Olschki, Florence]; Henry Walters, Baltimore, 1904.

EXHIBITIONS: Los Angeles County Museum of Art, "Exhibition of Medieval and Renaissance Illuminated Manscripts," 1953-1954, no. 64; Brussels, Bibliothèque Royale, "La Miniature Flamande. Le Mécénat de Philippe le Bon," 1959, no. 68; The Detroit Institute of Arts, "Masterpieces of Flemish Art: Van Eyck to Bosch," 1960, no. 202.

REFERENCES: L. Delisle, in *La Bibliofilia,* V, 1903-1904, pp. 269-275, ill.; De Ricci and Wilson, *Census,* I, p. 850, no. 5225; *Exhibition of Medieval and Renaissance Illuminated Manuscripts* (exhibition catalogue), Los Angeles, 1953-1954, no. 64; [L. J. M. Delaissé], *La Miniature Flamande. Le Mécénat de Philippe le Bon* (exhibition catalogue), Brussels, p. 74, no. 68, pl. 31; [Dorothy Miner], in *Flanders in the Fifteenth Century* (exhibition catalogue), Detroit, 1960, pp. 384-386, ill., p. 385.

PLATE XXXII

Lent by The Walters Art Gallery, Baltimore, ms. W. 305

**12  FRANCE, third quarter of the 15th century**

*Le Livre du Petit Artus*

Ms. in French: 218 vellum leaves in bâtarde script in 2 cols. with 37 half-page miniatures, H. 12 inches (30.5 cm.), W. 8-1/4 inches (21.0 cm.)

Along with romances of "le Grand Artus," or King Arthur, the story of Little Arthur, son of the "bon duc Jehan de Bretagne," belongs to that genre of heroic tales of chivalry much beloved during the late Middle Ages. This quite attractively illustrated manuscript without marginal decoration portrays the life of the chivalrous Arthur with accounts of battles, tournaments and episodes of courtly life in text and miniatures. It is usually dated ca. 1450, but a more conservative dating would place it ca. 1460 or later. Because of the very painterly, expressionistic style of its miniatures, it appears related to the school of Tours, which produced the "Maître François." It is interesting that the book once belonged to Jacques d'Armagnac, Duc de Nemours (d. 1477), for whom may have been produced an illustrated Boccaccio in a style close to the Maître François from which a miniature is shown in this exhibition (no. 13). One of the finest miniatures shows a delightful scene of a combat duel that takes place between two knights on the ground within an enclosed area after their horses have fallen. In another, a crowd of seemingly arrogant nobles and ladies is assembled for a marriage occasion.

EX COLLECTION: Jacques d'Armagnac, Duc de Nemours; [Payne and Mackinlay, 1795]; A. Davidson; Edward, first Baron Thurlaw; John Lewis Goldsmid (Sale, London, 1815, no. 160); [Dibdin]; John North (Sale, London, 1819, III, no. 808); Robert Lang (Sale, London, 1828, no. 1949); [Payne]; Sir Thomas Phillips, Middle Hill, Worcestershire and Thirlestaine House, Cheltenham, ms. 3633; [A. Rosenbach].

EXHIBITIONS: Baltimore Museum of Art, "Illuminated Books of the Middle Ages and Renaissance," 1949, no. 102.

REFERENCES: Twenty of the miniatures were used as illustrations for Lord Berners' English translation of the romance edited by E. V. Utterson, *Arthur of Little Britain*, London, 1814; W. R. Leech, in *Bulletin of the New York Public Library*, XXXII, 1928, pp. 391-396, ill.; De Ricci and Wilson, *Census*, II, p. 1333, no. 114; [Dorothy Miner], *Illuminated Manuscripts of the Middle Ages and Renaissance* (exhibition catalogue), Baltimore, 1949, p. 38, no. 102.

Lent by the Spencer Collection,
The New York Public Library,
Astor Lenox and Tilden Foundations, ms. 34

PLATES XLII, XLIII

**13  FRANCE (an artist close to the Maître François), ca. 1470**

*Queen Medusa Enthroned: single miniature from* Boccaccio, *Des clères et nobles femmes*

Tempera on vellum, H. 5-1/8 inches (13.0 cm.), W. 3-9/16 inches (9.0 cm.)

Formerly thought to be from a manuscript of the *Memorabilia* of Valerius Maximus, this miniature depicts Medusa, the lovely daughter of Phorcis, with attributes of wealth, beauty, and wisdom as described by Boccaccio in recounting the ancient Greek myth wherein Medusa is eventually transformed into a monster. It is only of recent discovery that this small miniature originally belonged to a manuscript Boccaccio, *Des clères et nobles femmes,* which is preserved in the Spencer Collection in the New York Public Library (ms. 33), and from which at least one and perhaps as many as three other miniatures besides this one have been removed. William Wixom, in noting Eleanor Spencer's discovery, also accepts as plausible her suggestion that the Boccaccio manuscript was made for Jacques d'Armagnac, in whose library another manuscript included in this exhibition also was formerly located (see no. 12). Previously, the coat-of-arms in the Spencer manuscript had been tentatively identified as that of Guilbert de La Fayette, Seigneur de Saint-Romain and Maréchal de France under Charles VII, or of Claude de Vissac of Auvergne.

This and the other miniatures in the Spencer manuscript document a production related to Tours of a certain period dominated by the personality known as "Maître François." The name derives from a sentence in a letter received in 1473 by the Governor of Paris, Charles de Gaucourt, from his scholar friend Robert Gaugin referring to the *Egregius Pictor Franciscus,* an illuminator who had just finished illustrating a copy of *Civitate Dei* of St. Augustine for de Gaucourt. The manuscript mentioned by Gaugin in the letter is today identified with the fine copy of St. Augustine's text in French translation now in the Bibliothèque Nationale in Paris (mss. fr. 18-19), and it is on the basis of the illustrations in this manuscript that the artistic personality of Maître François, active 1463-1481, has been uncovered in other manuscripts (see J. Wardrop, in *Apollo,* XV, 1932, pp. 76-82). But the problem of Maître François is extremely complex. Essentially the style of Jean Fouquet, the famous illuminator of Tours, and that of François are quite different. However, it is recognized that by the 1460's among a second generation of illuminators trained first in the late style of the Parisian-centered workshop of the Master of Bedford (see no. 8) the influence of Fouquet was almost inescapable. (For Maître François related to Paris and to the Bedford Master, see Eleanor P. Spencer, in *Parnassus,* XII, 1940, p. 31.)

Maître François, who must have headed a large workshop and who apparently was held in high esteem in his own time, is noted for his stunning decorative effects and for his impulse to render forms and atmosphere in technically brilliant series of interrupted brush strokes. Although his forms are not the solid ones of Fouquet, he certainly learned much about the effects of light from the great Tours artist. The style of the artist of "Queen Medusa Enthroned" shows an affinity with that of Maître François, and according to Eleanor Spencer this miniature must be related to the illustrations in another St. Augustine manuscript preserved in the Bibliothèque Municipale at Mâcon (mss. 1-2). Developed spatially in tapestry-like fashion, it is, in the words of William Wixom, "a pleasing and harmonious example of the last flowering of book illumination in which the page of the book is respected."

EX COLLECTION: Jacques d'Armagnac (?); Lord Mostyn, London (Sale, July 13, 1920, no. 9: entire manuscript); Mme. Th. Belin, Paris (Sale of the Boccaccio Manuscript without the present miniature, Paris, 1936); [Durlacher Brothers, New York, 1924].

EXHIBITIONS: Detroit Institute of Arts, "French Gothic Art of the Thirteenth to Fifteenth Century," 1928, no. 19; Brooklyn Museum of Art, "European Art 1450-1500," 1936, no. 94; Baltimore Museum of Art, "Illuminated Books of the Middle Ages and Renaissance," 1949, no. 110; Toronto, Royal Ontario Museum of Archaeology, "Medieval Illuminated Manuscripts," 1950; Pittsburgh, Pennsylvania, Carnegie Institute, "French Painting 1100-1900," 1951, no. 18; Los Angeles County Museum of Art, "Medieval and Renaissance Illuminated Manuscripts," 1953-1954; Cleveland Museum of Art, "Treasures from Medieval France," 1966-1967, no. VII-5.

REFERENCES: William M. Milliken, in Cleveland Museum of Art *Bulletin,* XII, 1925, p. 70, ill. p. 67; [W. R. Valentiner], *French Gothic Art of the Thirteenth to Fifteenth Century* (exhibition catalogue), Detroit, 1928, no. 19; *European Art 1450-1500* (exhibition catalogue), Brooklyn, 1936, no. 94, pl. 94; De Ricci and Wilson, *Census,* II, p. 1930; [Dorothy Miner], *Illuminated Books of the Middle Ages and Renaissance* (exhibition catalogue), Baltimore, 1949, p. 42, no. 110, pl. XLVI; *French Painting 1100-1900* (exhibition catalogue), Pittsburgh, 1951, no. 18, ill.; *Medieval and Renaissance Illuminated Manuscripts* (exhibition catalogue), Los Angeles, 1953-

1954; William D. Wixom, *Treasures from Medieval France* (exhibition catalogue), Cleveland, 1967, pp. 302, 383, no. VII-5, ill. p. 303.

Lent by The Cleveland Museum of Art,
Gift of J. L. H. Wade, 24.1015

PLATE XLII

14  NORTHERN FRANCE (atelier of the Maître François), ca. 1470

*The Last Judgment: single leaf from* Jean Chapuis, *Sept articles de la foi*

Tempera and burnished gold on vellum, H. 12-3/4 inches (27.3 cm.), W. 6-3/4 inches (17.2 cm.)

From the lower right corner of this miniature demons, like musicians in an orchestra pit, "rake" the damned of the resurrected from a stage of earth already being departed at the left by the blessed walking on air. Above the diagonally developed lower composition stretches a zone which disposes the heavenly beings in symmetrical fashion. Christ the Redeemer, seated on a rainbow and blocking the source of a radiant light, occupies the center. To His proper right are seated the female martyred saints, preceded by the Virgin Mary; to His left, the group of Apostles and other male saints, at the head of which are placed the two St. Johns. The text is kept from intruding upon the scene represented by being framed and by the use of golden rays to penetrate and fan across this area. Thus, the artist has introduced a composition of depth and brilliance into the page without destroying the integrity of the page as the leaf of a manuscript book.

These are characteristics the artist of this miniature shares with the miniaturist usually referred to as the Maître François, the *Egregius Pictor Franciscus* of Robert Gauguin's letter of 1473 (see no. 13). The composition itself recalls the miniature in the *Cité de dieu* of St. Augustine in the Bibliothèque Nationale in Paris, which documents the Maître François' style. Further, it has been connected with another copy of the *Cité de dieu* from the workshop of the Maître François as a work by the same hand. This second copy of St. Augustine's work to be associated with the Maître François is in the Museum Meermanno-Westreenianum in The Hague (ms. 10 A 11).

The influence of panel painting is apparent to a strong degree in the single-page "Last Judgment." It has been rightly pointed out, for example, that in its general arrangement of figures it shows similarities to Roger van der Weyden's famous altarpiece in Beaune. In its own way of adapting compositions of panel painting for the illustration of a book, as well as in the illusionistic technique and use of soft highlights in the figures, it betrays the influence of Jean Fouquet and the School of Tours. There is plasticity in the modelling of the figures and a vital force that animates them and gives them expression. Most remarkable is the treatment of light, which seems to penetrate the human forms as well as pale the colors of their garments. The qualities of illusionistic technique are conveyed especially well in the host of angels included above the head of the text, where monochromatic painting with lighter highlights still achieves full modelling of the figures.

EX COLLECTION: Sold at Sotheby's, London (June 1897, lot 550: Robson); S. Cockerell, 1906; sold at Sotheby's, April 3, 1957, lot 15).

EXHIBITIONS: London, Burlington Fine Arts Club, "Exhibition of Illuminated Manuscripts," 1908, no. 225; London, Royal Academy of Arts, "Exhibition of French Art 1200-1900," 1932, no. 621; Paris, "Chefs d'oeuvre de l'art française," 1935, no. 777; Chicago, Newberry Library, "French and Flemish Illuminated Manuscripts from Chicago Collections," 1969, no. 17.

REFERENCES: *Burlington Fine Arts Club, Exhibition of Illuminated Manuscripts* (exhibition catalogue), London, 1908, p. 110, no. 225; Thieme-Becker, *Allgemeines Künstlerlexikon*, XII,

p. 368; F. de Mely, *Les primitifs et leurs signatures*, Paris, 1913, p. 244 and fig. 214; *Exhibition of French Art 1200-1900* (exhibition catalogue), 1932, no. 621; *Chefs d'oeuvre de l'art française* (exhibition catalogue), Paris, 1937, no. 777; Herbert L. Kessler, *French and Flemish Illuminated Manuscripts from Chicago Collections* (exhibition catalogue), Chicago, 1969, p. (44), no. 17.

PLATE LIII                                     Lent by The Art Institute of Chicago

15   FRANCE (follower of Maître François), ca. 1480

*Book of Hours for use of Langres* (?)

Ms. in Latin: 169 vellum leaves in Gothic script with 17 large miniatures and various illuminated initials and border roundels, H. 9-1/4 inches (23.8 cm.), W. 6-1/2 inches (16.7 cm.)

The influences of Maître François (see no. 13) were felt in France beyond the confines of his workshop, especially among the provincial-within-provincial schools of illumination working in an eclectic manner during the last quarter of the fifteenth century. This Book of *Hours* shows a predilection for depicting the male subjects as rugged men with homely faces and the female subjects as pale, flat-faced women wearing placid expressions—in some ways caricatures of Maître François' own figures. The decorative effects, including tapestried walls, are those favored by his workshop and close associates, while other details, including the border roundels on the "Annunciation" page, reflect an eclectic tradition based ultimately on the late Master of Bedford style (see no. 8). Ours is an artist notably more at home with his conventional, but light and airy, landscapes than with the often archaic interiors which are lacking in atmosphere. The constituency of his landscapes is one both of convention of an earlier period and coloristic and atmospheric effects seen in the late fifteenth-century manuscripts of Jean and Jacques Colombe.

The comments here are based on Miss Sharon Foster's detailed discussion of the manuscript, which in most of its facets seems quite correct.

EX COLLECTION: [Harold A. Levinson].

REFERENCES: Sharon L. Foster, *The Kansas University Hours of the Virgin,* 1965 (unpublished master's thesis, deposited in the University of Kansas Library).

                                              Lent by The University of Kansas Libraries,
PLATES LI, LII                      Special Collections, Solon E. Summerfield Fund

16   FRANCE (Lyonnais or Savoie), ca. 1480-1485

*Proverbes en rimes*

Ms. in French: 91 paper leaves with 182 pen drawings, H. 7-7/8 inches (20.0 cm.), W. 5-1/8 inches (13.0 cm.)

Popular illustrated books of France are easily overlooked because of the wealth of sumptuously illustrated French manuscripts preserved from the Later Middle Ages. But as books became more and more widely available to the non-aristocratic public, the appeal of unpretentiously hand-illustrated books determined a type of production that deserves mention as a part of the life and culture of late Medieval France. Because the popular illustrated books were not regarded with the same concern for preservation as were manuscripts of the precious variety, they have survived only rarely. A very unusual manuscript copy of the popular *Ars Moriendi* included in this exhibition (no. 17) holds claim as a characteristic example of the widely circulated religious tract. More rare, however, is the illustrated secular work known as the *Proverbes en rimes.*

The *Proverbes en rimes,* a collection of rhymed proverbs in French to each of which is drawn an illustration, is recognized as the earliest surviving member of a group of books illustrating French proverbs in verse. It is a creation of a sort that looks forward to the emblem books of the Renaissance, those storehouses of iconography and symbolism which influenced artists in their presentation of thematic material. Chiefly on the basis of the costume of the figures in the pen-drawn illustrations the manuscript has been dated ca. 1480-1485, or around the time of King Charles VIII. It has been localized to eastern France, to the Lyonnais or Savoie.

The study of the manuscript by Frank and Miner is both complete and authoritative. Among the illustrations are recognized three hands, to the best of which can be attributed an undefinable pictorial charm. Characteristic examples of his work are the illustrations to the proverbs ending with the lines, "Link after link the coat (of mail) is made at length" (fol. 10 verso), "While the dog pisses, the wolf escapes to the woods" (fol. 11 recto), and "The house shows its owner" (fol. 72 verso). The latter represents a well-kept house with a warm hearth, a cabinet on which shining metalware is neatly placed, and a master who is loved by his animal pets. The most interesting aspect of the drawing style is the similarity in the technique of modelling to that of engravings. The figures and objects appear flat but are modelled with many short strokes and cross-hatchings near the outlines. Frank and Miner have noticed that the slightly later manuscript of the *Proverbes en rimes* in the British Museum (Ms. Add. 37527) contains nearly identical illustrations in a similar style.

EX COLLECTION: [Gruel, Paris]; Henry Walters, Baltimore, 1905.

REFERENCES: De Ricci and Wilson, *Census,* I, p. 848; Grace Frank and Dorothy Miner, *Proverbes en Rimes,* Baltimore, 1937; Timothy Foote, *The World of Brueghel ca. 1525-1569,* New York, 1969, p. 142.

Lent by The Walters Art Gallery,
PLATES LVI, LVII                                      Baltimore, ms. W. 313

17   FRANCE, late 15th century

*Ars Moriendi*

Ms. in Latin: 11 vellum leaves in Gothic script with 6 colored drawings, H. 6-11/16 inches (17.0 cm.), W. 5-1/8 inches (13.0 cm.)

For fifteenth-century readers the *Ars Moriendi* was undoubtedly the single most popular text describing the death experience. The text has been recognized as a late derivative of earlier Medieval writings of the Church on the subject, and in fact it served the Church as a means of calming the excessive fear of death that had possessed the European populace since about the middle of the fourteenth century. Other illustrated manuscript versions of the text are known, and it is believed that the woodcuts in the famous blockbook edition which issued from presses in the Netherlands and brought the text into wide circulation were also based on manuscript illustrations. But the manuscript exhibited reverses this order and copies the woodcuts from the blockbook edition. The date of 1466 recently established for the blockbook *Ars Moriendi* therefore establishes a *terminus post quem* for this provincial, but charmingly and naïvely illustrated French manuscript (see Alan Stephenson, *The Quincentennial of the Nether-landish Blockbooks* [exhibition catalogue], London, British Museum, 1967).

EX COLLECTION: [Quaritch, London].

REFERENCES: *Catalogue of Illuminated and Other Manuscripts, 1930* (catalogue of the dealer Quaritch), November, 1939, no. 1; W. H. Bond and C. U. Faye, Supplement to the *Census of Medieval and Renaissance Manuscripts in the United States and Canada,* New York, 1962, p. 208, no. 87.

PLATE LI                                  Lent by The Boston Public Library, ms. 1514

18   FLANDERS (Bruges?), ca. 1465-1470

*The Meeting of Priam and Helen before the Gates of Troy: single leaf from* Jehan de Courcy, *Chronique universelle dit la bouquechardière*

Tempera and burnished gold on vellum, H. 15-3/8 inches (39.0 cm.), W. 11 inches (27.9 cm.)

Jehan de Courcy, Seigneur de Bourc-Achard, who was active between the years 1399-1431, compiled a book of stories based on history and legend of ages past which he called *Chronique universelle dit la bouquechardière.* The text was often copied later in the fifteenth century, and this page with a miniature depicting Helen meeting King Priam upon her first arrival from Greece comes from such a later copy of Jehan de Courcy's work. The measurements of the page correspond to the usual large size of manuscripts produced in Flanders, especially during the time of Philip the Bold. The composition of the miniature is almost identical to that on fol. 84 in volume I of the manuscript copy of the same text now in the Pierpont Morgan Library, New York, ms. M. 214 (cf. *Flanders in the Fifteenth Century* [exhibition catalogue], Detroit, 1960, pp. 388-390, ill.). The Morgan manuscript was produced in the workshop of Philippe de Mazarolles, court painter to Charles the Bold, Duke of Burgundy, probably at Bruges. In both miniatures the places of entry of the two processions, right and left, are the same; the placement of principal figures is similar; in each there is a view across the harbor, in which boats are anchored, toward the other side where the bodies of soldiers are strewn on the ground; and behind the walls of the city gate at the right is seen a view down the street at an angle. The style of the present miniature seems earlier than that of the Morgan manuscript, which is dated ca. 1470. It bears some resemblance to the style of Liévin van Lathem, a Ghent miniaturist whose presence in Bruges is also documented, and whose work is often mistaken for that of Philippe de Mazarolles. One wonders if the manuscript from which this single page came might actually have served as the model for the Morgan manuscript, or whether the miniatures in both depend closely on a common model. Dissimilarities exist between the style of the scripts and between the wording of the two corresponding pages of text. The present example is distinguished by the playful human and animal forms depicted in its borders—the wild man armed with a shield and club and riding a griffon, the mermaid combing her hair, and the dog sniffing at something.

EX COLLECTION: Joseph Brummer, New York.

EXHIBITIONS: Pittsburgh, Pennsylvania, Carnegie Institute, "French Painting 1100-1900," no. 17; Buffalo, New York, Albright-Knox Art Gallery, "Art in the Book," 1953-1954, no. 24; Berkeley, University of California, University Art Gallery, "Medieval and Renaissance Illuminated Manuscripts from the Xth to the early XVth Centuries," 1963, no. 36.

REFERENCES: William H. Milliken, in Cleveland Museum of Art *Bulletin,* XXXII, 1945, pp. 135-137, ill. p. 133; *French Painting 1100-1900* (exhibition catalogue), Pittsburgh, 1951, no. 17, ill.; *Art in the Book* (exhibition catalogue), Buffalo, 1953-1954, no. 24; *Medieval and Renaissance Illuminated Manuscripts from the Xth to the early XVth Centuries* (exhibition catalogue), Berkeley, 1963, no. 36, pl. XXXIII; W. H. Bond and C. U. Faye, *Supplement to the*

*Census of Medieval and Renaissance Manuscripts in the United States and Canada*, New York, 1962, p. 429.

PLATE XXXIV

## 19 FLANDERS, 1472-1477

Honoré Bonet, *L'Arbre des Batailles;* Diego de Valera, *Espejo de Verdadera Nobleza, trans. into French by* Hugo de Salucces; *and other miscellaneous texts*

Ms. in French: 218 vellum leaves in bâtarde script with 1 large and 11 small miniatures, 63 painted armorial bearings, H. 13-3/8 inches (34.0 cm), W. 8-3/8 inches (21.0 cm.)

The text that consumes nearly half of the total number of pages of this manuscript, the *Arbre des Batailles* by Honoré Bonet, is one of the most earnest, sincere, and compassionate secular writings of the Later Middle Ages. It is dedicated to the ideal of proper conduct between men and nations in battles, both private and general. Never having scurried once to the lines of battle or taken part in a duel or tournament, its author, an ecclesiastic and prior of Selonnet in Provence, has derived what is essentially a law of nations, similar to our modern Geneva Convention Treaty, from the Medieval code of chivalrous conduct. Yet Bonet is not concerned with legal bases or consequences, and the series of questions he raises with regard to the combatant's behavior, whether on the battlefield or in his own back yard, are appeals to the humane instincts of people like himself. This manuscript copy, which has added to it the Diego de Valera text, together with a prologue, in the Salucces translation (as well as the *Comment on fait de nouvel un empereur par election,* Thomas of Gloucester's *Manière de faire champ à l'outrance,* King Philip IV's ordinance of 1306 regulating a duel *en champs fermé,* a Rules of Order for the installation of a King of Arms and of heralds, *La mannière de faire les tournaments,* an Office of Arms or funeral of the nobility describing obsequies of Gerard de Mortagne in 1391, a description of the making of a King of Arms of France and his duties, and ordinances relating to the army of the Duchy of Burgundy) was written between 1472 and 1476, probably for Charles the Bold, Duke of Burgundy, and includes a full-page presentation scene for the title page and one miniature at the beginning of each of the various texts. In spirit and in mode of illustration these belong to the repertory of illustrations for chivalrous romances.

EX COLLECTION: Charles the Bold, Duke of Burgundy(?); George Hibbert (Sale, March 30, 1829, lot 2707); Sir Thomas Phillipps, Middle Hill, Worcestershire and Thirlestaine House, Cheltenham; D. M. Colman; [Stonehill].

REFERENCES: Yale University Library *Gazette*, XXIX, 1955, pp. 106-107, 109-110, ill.; W. H. Bond and C. U. Faye, Supplement to the *Census of Medieval and Renaissance Manuscripts in the United States and Canada,* New York, 1962, pp. 43-44, no. 230.

PLATE XXXVIII

## 20 LILLE (?), 1476

Caesar, *Les commentaires, traduite par Jean du Chesne*

Ms. in French: 30 vellum and 231 paper leaves, written in red and black bâtarde script in 2 cols., with 10 large and three small miniatures, H. 14-3/4 inches (37.4 cm.), W. 10-11/16 inches (27.2 cm.)

Jean du Chesne, the translator, compiler, and copyist employed by Charles the

Bold, Duke of Burgundy, finished his translation of Caesar's *Commentaries* in Lille in 1473, as we are told in a note at the end of his own transcription, now in the British Museum (Royal Ms. 16 G viii). The original translation and transcription was dedicated to Charles the Bold, the ducal motto, *"à james" (à jamais)*, appearing on the binding; but apparently it belonged to Philippe de Clèves, Seigneur de Ravenstein (see John W. Bradley, *A Dictionary of Miniaturists, Illuminators, Calligraphers, and Copyists,* Reprint of the London, 1887-1889 edition, New York, 1958, I, pp. 227-228). Bradley notes that another copy written and illustrated in 1474 at Lille is now in the Royal Library at Copenhagen. A third copy is in the Library of the Marquess of Bath at Longleat, Somersetshire (I am indebted to Dorothy Miner of the Walters Art Gallery in Baltimore for this information), and the present copy, written by Hellin de Burchgrave in 1476 for Jacques Douche, a counsellor of Charles the Bold, is the fourth known copy. A colophon in our manuscript repeats the note written by Jean du Chesne in the original transcription and states that Hellin de Burchgrave has written the copy after the original (at the request of the Duke's counsellor) in 1476.

Jean du Chesne's translation is actually that of Books I-VII (in eight) of Caesar's *Gallic Wars* plus Book VIII (his book IX), or the pseudo-Caesar "Gallic War." To these translations have been added du Chesne's own prologues to the two parts, and following his Book IX, his later life of Caesar based on Lucian and Suetonius. The full-page miniature at the beginning of the present manuscript depicts the translator-author presenting his book to his patron, Charles the Bold, following the custom for subsequent copies of books originally dedicated to illustrious patrons. Charles is depicted wearing the collar and pendant of the Order of the Golden Fleece, which had been founded by Philip the Good on the occasion of his marriage to Isabella of Portugal in 1430; behind his throne appears the device of the order, the flame-sparking *briquet* of Burgundy. The colophon does not state whether Hellin de Burchgrave wrote his copy at Lille. But on the basis of the style of the miniatures and on the reference in the colophon to Jacques Douche as Charles the Bold's "Watregrave et moermaistre de flandres," the localization of the writing and illustration to Burgundy (sale catalogue of the Phillipps collection) seems unnecessary. The miniatures are executed in *grisaille* with tints of colors added, a technique that was often practiced in northern France and Flanders. The scenes of the smaller miniatures include Caesar's birth, his crossing of the Rubicon in 49 B.C., the battles of his Roman legions in Gaul and their occupation of Britain, and Caesar's death.

EX COLLECTION: Jacques Douche, 1476; Prince Eugene of Savoy; Imperial Library, Vienna, 1788; Sir Thomas Phillipps, Middle Hill, Worcestershire and Thirlestaine House, Cheltenham, ms. 4759; D. M. Colman; [Stonehill].

REFERENCES: Sale catalogue of the Sir Thomas Phillipps Collection at Sotheby's, London, July 1, 1946, p. 20, no. 25.

Lent by Yale University Library,
New Haven, Connecticut

PLATE XXXVII

21   FRANCE or FLANDERS, ca. 1475

*The Battle of l'Écluse: single leaf from* Froissart, *Chroniques* (?)

Tempera and burnished gold on vellum, H. 9-1/16 inches (23.0 cm.), W. 6-1/4 inches (15.8 cm.)

In spite of the small size of this single illustrated page, unlikely for a manuscript containing Froissart's interminable text, the subject of the naval battle between the English and the French at l'Écluse would be appropriate as part of the illustrations to a *Chroniques*. The hand in the miniature is not distinguished, but there is a charming pictorial manner to the illustration. The artist has lined up the ships alternating French and English. He shows that the French ships are larger and of better construction; he is faithful to the proper arms on the streamers flown on the respective ships, and displays a particular interest in the fact that the English are using longbows while the French are using crossbows. To enforce this latter notion, he has placed two vignettes in the lower border, one of an Englishman drawing a longbow at a Frenchman and the other of a Frenchman returning the shot with his superior crossbow. The stylized treatment of the ripples in the water and the untiring efforts to make every suit of armor reflect light are most interesting. The border design reveals a classic order and symmetry that are more usual in manuscripts from northern France and Flanders around mid-century.

EX COLLECTION: Grenville Kane, Tuxedo Park, New York.

LITERATURE: De Ricci and Wilson, *Census*, II, p. 1900; Princeton University Library *Chronicle*, XXVII, 1966, p. 190, no. 67.

PLATE XXXV

Lent by Princeton University Library, Princeton, New Jersey, Kane ms. 58

22  FRANCE, late 15th century

*A battle scene: single leaf from* Gerard de Roussillion, *Chanson de Geste*

Tempera on vellum, H. 15-3/8 inches (38.0 cm.), W. 11 inches (28.0 cm.)

The half-page miniature on this leaf from a prose version of Roussillion's secular work represents a military encounter between troups of armored soldiers before a dense, green forest. The large size of the page and the vivid rendering of a large-scale scene of battle are typical of the manuscripts produced in the ateliers of northern France adjacent to Burgundy-controlled Flanders.

EX COLLECTION: Arnold Mettler, Sankt Gallen.

REFERENCES: Sale catalogue of Sotheby's, London, April 27, 1937, no. 289.

Lent by The Lehman Collection, New York

23  BRUGES, before 1478

*A Scribe Writing and the Author Presenting his Book: single miniature from an illustrated manuscript*

Brush and blue watercolor on grey prepared paper, H. 6-7/16 inches (16.4 cm.), W. 7-1/4 inches (18.5 cm.)

This miniature has been cut from the title page of a manuscript, now lost, of which eight of the other miniatures are also preserved. Two are in the Van der Feer Ladèr Collection in Baarn, Holland, and the remaining six, formerly in the collection of Fritz Lugt, are now in the Institut Néerlandais in Paris (cf. *Bourgondische Pracht* [exhibition catalogue], Amsterdam, 1951, no. 112). The two-part scene here includes, writing at his desk, a bespectacled scribe whom Elizabeth Mongan has sought to identify as David Aubert, the celebrated editor, translator and scribe of Philip the Good of Burgundy. This tentative identification is no doubt the source of the confusion in connecting the miniature with a manuscript copy of Wauquelin's *Girart de Roussillon*, which in part served Aubert for the *Chroniques de Charlemagne* he presented to Philip the Good in

1458 (see [L. M. J. Delaissé], *La Miniature Flamande. Le Mécénat de Philippe le Bon* [exhibition catalogue], Brussels, 1959, p. 97, no. 970). The other known miniatures cut from the same manuscript actually represent scenes from the Life of the Virgin and the Passion of Christ and as such are inappropriate for the illustration of either a *Girart de Roussillon* or a *Chroniques de Charlemagne*.

Boon has shown that an illustrated manuscript of Ludolphus de Saxonia's *Vita Christi,* now in the Museum Czartoryska in Cracow (ms. 2919), copies some of the miniatures from the same manuscript which contained the present dedication miniature. The Cracow manuscript, made for Guillaume de Ternay, Provost of Lille and from 1475 "Maréchal de logis" of Charles the Bold, heir to Philip the Good, is dated 1478. The present miniature, therefore, and the others originally forming part of the book from which the Cracow illustrations were copied, must have been produced prior to that time.

Despite Boon's doubts that the person represented receiving the book is Duke Philip the Good, there is little reason to believe that anyone else would be depicted as enthroned like the Burgundian Duke, with or without the *toison d'or* insignia that are lacking here. But the style of the miniature is too late for the period of Philip the Good (d. 1467), and were it indeed to represent him it would have to have been copied posthumously from the opening miniature of a book dedicated to Philip during his lifetime. This could easily be the case.

The artist of this miniature is one of the many miniaturists working in Ghent and Bruges during the late fifteenth century who were profoundly influenced by the painter Hugo van der Goes of Ghent. Both Boon and Haverkamp-Begemann relate its technique to drawings in the style of Hugo. The extremely elongated figures are but exaggerated forms of Hugo's figures for the pair of organ shutters painted for Sir Edward Bonkil and sent to Scotland. This and the other preserved miniatures from the same manuscript exhibit the style of yet other miniatures which have been attached to the name of Alexander Bening of the Ghent-Bruges School, but the attribution of miniatures to this artist is very problematic (see Friedrich Winkler, *Die flämische Buchmalerei des XV. und XVI. Jahrhunderts,* Leipzig, 1925, p. 117). Haverkamp-Begemann agrees that Alexander, the father of Simon Bening, is not their author.

EX COLLECTION: [William H. Schab, New York]; Erwin Rosenthal; Lessing J. Rosenwald, Jenkintown, Pennsylvania, 1946.

EXHIBITIONS: Washington, National Gallery of Art, "Rosenwald Collection. An Exhibition of Recent Acquisitions," 1960, no. 26.

REFERENCES: Catalogue of the dealer William H. Schab, New York, 1942, no. 3; [Elizabeth Mongan], *Rosenwald Collection. An Exhibition of Recent Acquisitions* (exhibition catalogue), Washington, 1960, pp. 11, 32, no. 26, ill.; K. G. Boon in *Nederlands Kunsthistorisch Jaarboek,* III, 1950-1951, p. 95; Egbert Haverkamp-Begemann, in *Great Drawings of All Time,* edited by Ira Moskowitz, New York, 1962, II, no. 471.

Lent by The National Gallery of Art,

PLATE XXXIX       Rosenwald Collection, Washington, B. 13.515

24 BRUGES, ca. 1490

*Blessed Virgins Entering Paradise: single leaf from a Book of Hours*

Tempera on vellum, H. 6-1/4 inches (15.9 cm.), W. 4-5/8 inches (11.8 cm.)

The temptation for Northern fifteenth century illuminators to turn the decorations of the manuscript page into pictures inspired by the style of contemporary panel paintings, and together with this the ever-increasing, drowning noises of early printing presses, posed serious threats to the life of the illustrated manuscript and finally cast it from the peak where it earlier had stood as an importantly creative artistic enterprise. This leaf from a late fifteenth-century Flemish Book of *Hours* shows the signs of over-exposure to panel paintings, but it also exhibits a curious and relatively new interpretation of the page as composed of multiple overlapping segments of infinite space. The principal scene of the Wise Virgins being welcomed by Christ at the Gates of Paradise occupies the space usually allotted the single miniature, while below and at the left, in the areas normally given over to border decoration of vine scrolls, have been added further scenes that consume all the available space between the frame of the principal miniature and the outer margin of the border. The border margin itself is treated as a frame that cuts off figures from view; hence, the result is a frame-within-a-frame arrangement that appears like a collage of surfaces of panel paintings. The left and lower frame-lines of the principal miniature double as frame-lines for the other representations, lines behind which figures can disappear and on either side of which continuing space can be imagined. Ingeniously, the artist has provided the key to the interpretation of the role of the frame to capture only a detail of a greater imaginary space; for at the upper right, where it appears at first he has disregarded the frame, he helps imagination along by actually showing part of the building which is supposed to be closed off from view by the limiting device of the frame. We are to imagine that the arbitrarily placed frame around the principal scene could be moved in any direction and would correspondingly take in more or less of the scene inside it while reducing or expanding the amount seen of the scenes outside it.

This intriguing playfulness with the idea of space, which seems the manuscript illuminator's attempt to do the panel painter one better, is in the end, of course, more than the page as the leaf of a manuscript could withstand. The artist has carried the illustration far beyond the limits of function and therefore has violated the integrity of the page. Yet we can see this and the many late fifteenth-century Flemish examples very much like it as the logical development out of earlier apparent tendencies. The "Last Judgment" page from Jean Chapuis' *Sept articles de la foi,* on exhibition (no. 14), already leads us to imagine space around and behind the framed text set within the miniature and appearing suspended in the sky. But there the representation and the text are kept relevant to each other and to the page. The text is an integral part of the miniature and is attached by means of the choirs of angels that hover above it, but at the sides and bottom figures are not allowed to disappear behind it. Later, especially in manuscripts of the Ghent-Bruges School, buildings and landscapes appear to extend behind a tablet of text and are cut off by it. In the Book of *Hours* in the National Library in Madrid (ms. Vit. 25-5; cf. Otto Pächt, *The Master of Mary of Burgundy,* London [1948], pl. 25), a work contemporary with the present manuscript leaf, the strip of text is painted to look as though it is tied with strings to various points along the frame of the miniature and is thus held secure in such a way that it appears to obscure parts of the scenes represented around and behind it. The Calendar pages of the famous *Grimani Breviary* (Venice, Biblioteca di San Marco), associated with Gerard Horenbout and Simon Bening and dating around the second decade of the sixteenth century, continue the use of the multiple overlapping segments of infinite space.

Although the present miniature reveals the novel spatial effects popularized by the miniaturists of Ghent and Bruges, its style of painting has suggested connections with the area around Brussels to Carmen Gómez-Moreno. The iconography of the three scenes and the inscription *VENITE OMNES VIRGINES* beneath the angel in the lower representation indicate that the page of illustrations was to accompany a prayer for all virgin saints in the suffrages of the Book of *Hours*. The scene at the left, which shares a common sky with the principal scene, depicts the virgins encircling Christ in the *hortus conclusis* in heavenly Paradise. In the lower scene, the dark-clad abbess who has been identified as St. Bridget of Sweden is reminiscent of similar heavily-robed, seated figures seen in early fifteenth-century Parisian manuscripts and the two Frick "Pietàs." Perhaps the figure is to be interpreted as a conscious reference to the past (for a similar figure introduced as an archaic reference in contemporary sculpture, see no. 70).

EXHIBITIONS: Paris, Musée de l'Orangerie, "La Collection Lehman de New York," 1957, no. 162; Cincinnati Art Museum, "The Lehman Collection, New York," 1959, no. 340; New York, Metropolitan Museum of Art (Cloisters), "Medieval Art from Private Collections," 1968-1969, no. 10.

REFERENCES: [Sylvie Béguin], in *La Collection Lehman de New York* (exhibition catalogue), Paris, 1957, p. 111, no. 162, pl. LXXVII; *The Lehman Collection, New York* (exhibition catalogue), Cincinnati, 1959, p. 32, no. 340, ill.; Carmen Gómez-Moreno, *Medieval Art from Private Collections* (exhibition catalogue), New York, 1968-1969, no. 10, ill.

PLATE LVIII                          Lent by The Lehman Collection, New York

25   FLANDERS, late 15th century

*The Crucifixion: single miniature from a Missal*

Tempera on vellum, H. 10-5/8 inches (27.0 cm.), W. 7-1/2 inches (19.0 cm.)

This painted miniature is thought to have been cut out of the canon page of a manuscript Missal. The artist, whose monogram consisting of an *I.* superimposed on an *M.* is painted in gold in the lower right-hand corner of the miniature, has not yet been identified, nor have other miniatures bearing this monogram come to light. It has been suggested that a North Netherlandish artist perhaps working in Ghent during the time Joos van Gent and Hugo van der Goes were active is responsible for this work, but neither part of this suggestion seems tenable. A date in the last decade of the fifteenth century and a center somewhat remote from either Bruges or Ghent—perhaps Antwerp—would seem more feasible. In some details, especially the Magdalen at Christ's feet and the St. John shown supporting the swooning Virgin, the miniature shows relationships to the early style of Quentin Metsys, who was active in the Scheldt city. Certainly the halos of radiating gold lines which had been abandoned earlier in the century have been brought back along with the decorative gold borders on costumes, as part of the general Eyckian revival that took place in the late fifteenth century. The figures are quite broadly handled, and there seems to be a fairly extensive underdrawing, like that of a panel painting. This broad conception is felt particularly in the figure of the richly costumed man at the right who holds a scroll with the inscription: *vere filius dei erat iste:*. This miniature has a particular iconographic interest, for besides depicting the usual motif of the souls of the good and bad thieves being removed by an angel and a demon, respectively, it also shows the influence of the Last Judgment theme by raising the good soul above the arm of the cross and making the demon descend with the bad soul.

EXHIBITIONS: Paris, Musée de l'Orangerie, "La Collection Lehman de New York," 1957, no. 173; Cincinnati Art Museum, "The Lehman Collection, New York," 1959, no. 338.

REFERENCES: *La Collection Lehman de New York* (exhibition catalogue), Paris, 1957, p. 116, no. 173, pl. LXXVIII; *The Lehman Collection, New York* (exhibition catalogue), Cincinnati, 1959, p. 32, no. 338, ill.

PLATE LIX                          Lent by The Lehman Collection, New York

# PAINTINGS

26    Circle of ROGER VAN DER WEYDEN, second half of the 15th century

*The Adoration of the Shepherds*

Oil on panel, H. 32-1/2 inches (82.6 cm.), W. 24 inches (61.0 cm.)

Of the two leading Netherlandish painters of the first half of the fifteenth century —Robert Campin and Jan van Eyck—Campin, it appears, received the more immediate distinction of having his style perpetuated in the second half of the century through a more than noteworthy pupil. In 1432, Jacques Daret and Roger van der Weyden, two young painters and natives of Tournai, completed their apprenticeship with Robert Campin, each having served with him for five years. Little is known about Jacques Daret beyond October 18, 1432, when he was admitted to the painters' guild at Tournai as master and simultaneously elected Dean of the guild. We know of his presence in Lille, Bruges, and Arras until 1468, when documents cease to mention him, and we know that among other things he designed tapestries for the Abbey of Saint Vaast at Arras. However, our knowledge of his work rests solely on the four paintings he executed for the decoration of a carved altarpiece commissioned in 1434 by Jean du Clercq, Abbot of St. Vaast (the paintings are now preserved in Berlin, Paris, and Lugano). Roger van der Weyden, on the other hand, became the celebrated City Painter of Brussels and left us numerous works that testify to his having been the leading painter who spanned the two halves of the fifteenth century.

Max J. Friedländer, the Nestor of studies in early Netherlandish painting, left a certificate attributing the "Adoration of the Shepherds," on exhibition, to Jacques Daret. If the attribution is correct, we are then forced to believe that Daret became a follower and imitator of his former colleague from Robert Campin's workshop, Roger van der Weyden, for the work is based on the central panel of Roger's *Bladelin Altarpiece* of shortly after 1452 (see Erwin Panofsky, *Early Netherlandish Painting,* Cambridge, Mass., 1953, pp. 276-278, figs. 335-340).

The altarpiece by Roger was commissioned by Peter Bladelin, Receiver General of Finance to Duke Philip the Good of Burgundy and founder of the town of Middelburg, northeast of Bruges. The work was destined for the church of the new town Bladelin began building in 1448. The central panel depicts the "Nativity," in which the donor plays a role equally prominent with those of the Virgin and St. Joseph. In the background appears an idealized version of the town prospect of Middelburg. Panofsky noticed that for this central panel Roger revived a composition by his former master, Robert Campin—the Dijon "Nativity" of more than thirty years before, and the same painting whose composition had been more literally borrowed by Jacques Daret for his altarpiece of 1434-1435.

Roger's *Bladelin Altarpiece* is seen reflected in numerous later works by followers. The central panel of a triptych in the Cloisters of the Metropolitan Museum in New York, for example, combines Roger's central panel and right wing into one setting. Herbert Kessler found the Roger work the source for a miniature in a manuscript from the atelier of William Vrelant in the Allen Memorial Art Museum in Oberlin, Ohio, noting also the present version painted on panel. In spite of the fact that our painting includes the shepherds in place of the donor, it is more faithful to Roger's composition than other known works modelled after it. It retains the positions of the principal figures and the architecture set at an oblique angle to the picture plane. It preserves the symbolic significance of many of the motifs of Roger's work inspired by the writings of St.

Bridget and Pseudo-Bonaventure. For instance, the marble column at the corner of the stable does not lose its significance as the column upon which the Virgin Mary was said to have leaned at the hour of her labor, and against which Christ was later supposed to have been flagellated during the Passion (Panofsky's interpretation), as it does by being doubled in the altarpiece at the Cloisters in New York. The candle held by Joseph represents the material light which, according to St. Bridget, was obscured by the divine light emanating from the newborn Infant.

The horizontal layout of Roger van der Weyden's composition has been changed to vertical in the "Adoration of the Shepherds." The result is a change of proportions and loss of solidity in the architecture and a crowding at the right with figures disproportionate in scale to those of the Virgin and Joseph. Curiously, the eldest shepherd removing his hat is reminiscent, in facial type, of the Joseph in Campin's Dijon "Nativity," and the other shepherds also exhibit Campinian characteristics. The trio of angels that appear above the roof in the Dijon "Nativity," in Jacques Daret's "Nativity" from the *Saint Vaast Altarpiece,* and again in the *Bladelin Altarpiece,* have been omitted.

EX COLLECTION: Minneapolis Institute of Arts.

EXHIBITIONS: San Diego Museum of Arts, "The Madonna in Art," 1957; Westmorland County Museum of Art, 1960.

REFERENCES: Herbert L. Kessler, in Allen Memorial Art Museum *Bulletin,* Oberlin, XXIII, 1966, p. 121, ill. p. 120, fig. 8.

PLATE XXVII                                          Lent by Victor Spark, New York

27  VRANCKE VAN DER STOCKT, second half of the 15th century

*A Kneeling Donor with St. John the Baptist*

Oil on panel, H. 17-3/4 inches (42.6 cm.), W. 8-1/8 inches (20.6 cm.)

A conventional representation of a kneeling donor and his patron saint—here St. John the Baptist—and New Testament scenes seldom represented in Netherlandish painting are combined in this left wing from a small triptych. In a landscape setting behind the donor is developed in narrative sequence the story of the Temptation of Christ. Closest to the foreground, Satan, in the guise of a holy man, a monk, offers Christ the stone, while immediately behind them, the dove of the Holy Ghost appears to Christ. In the distance is related Christ's ascent to the top of the cliff, where Satan, still clad in a monk's habit, is made to float in air. Angels adoring Christ are depicted below the cliff. Finally, at the background left, Christ and Satan are seen standing on top of the tower of the temple, which has the appearance of an elaborate Gothic church set within the fortified walls of a city. The representation of Christ's temptation is known in other Netherlandish examples, but almost all are of later date. For instance, it appears among the numerous panels that made up Juan de Flandes' altarpiece for Isabella la Católica, executed in Castile. The motif of adoring angels is the principal subject of an early sixteenth century painting by Jacob Cornelisz. van Oostsanen in the Suermondt-Museum in Aachen, a work in which the three main elements of the narrative represented in the present work also appear. The explanation for the use of the Temptation of Christ in the present work is its connection with St. John the Baptist, for the sequence follows chronologically the Baptism of Christ. St. John appears as the baptizer of Christ, clad in the camel's hair coat he wore while in the wilderness. In an early sixteenth-century painting by Jan Joest van Calcar the Temptation is related pictorially to the Baptism scene (cf. Karel Smits,

30

*Iconografie van de Nederlandse Primitieven,* Amsterdam, 1933, p. 72). But more directly related is the Baptism panel in Roger van der Weyden's *St. John Altarpiece* of ca. 1452-1455 (Berlin, Staatliche Museen). There the Temptation is represented in a series of three sculptural reliefs in the archivolts of an archway which frames the narrative, and also symbolic scene of Baptism (see Carl Birkmeyer, in *The Art Bulletin,* XLIII, 1961, pp. 1-20, 99-112). It should be stressed that Roger's altarpiece is a nearly isolated early example in which the Temptation is represented in connection with St. John the Baptist; hence, it is especially relevant to the discussion of a work in the style of Roger, like the present painting.

The close stylistic relationship to works by Roger van der Weyden is the basis for attributing this and other works to Vrancke van der Stockt (or Vranck van der Stock), a Brussels artist born before 1424 to the artist Jan van der Stockt, and who died in 1495 (see Hulin de Loo, in *Biographie Nationale de Belgique,* XXIV, 1926-1927, col. 66 ff.). Vrancke took over his father's Brussels workshop in 1444 (the same year Roger van der Weyden's teacher, Robert Campin, died and three years following Jan van Eyck's decease). Van der Stockt's exact relationship to Roger van der Weyden can only be surmised, but it is a well documented fact that when Roger died in 1464 the city fathers of Brussels voted that he take over Roger's old position as *stad schildere,* or City Painter, a position that presumably was created for Roger sometime before or during 1436. In 1436, the city fathers had agreed not to replace Roger when he died, for they seemingly were convinced they would never find his equal; but in 1464 they either ignored or reversed their earlier decision. Vrancke, who is presumed to have worked with Roger in Brussels and imitated the great master's style, was a likely choice.

Stylistic as well as iconographic qualities relate the present altarpiece wing to Roger van der Weyden's *St. John Altarpiece.* The St. John in the present painting, though shown in a slightly different pose than Roger's figure in the Baptism scene of his work, is reminiscent of the older work in drapery, position of the legs, physiognomy, and expressive hands. It is perhaps significant that a drawing in Roger's style, produced in connection with the *St. John Altarpiece* and showing the head and right arm in addition to the lower legs of Roger's baptizing St. John, is preserved (New York, The Lehman Collection; reproduced in the catalogue of the sale at Sotheby's, London, June 30, 1948, no. 153, frontispiece). It characteristically emphasizes the forelock of hair on the head that is also a prominent feature in the present painting. Perhaps Vrancke van der Stockt had access to this and other similar drawings, if not to the *St. John Altarpiece* itself or the smaller replica of it which is now in the Staedelsches Kunstinstitut in Frankfurt (one of these is probably identical with the triptych donated to the Church of St. James in Bruges by Baptiste del Agnelli in 1476). Finally, it may be said that the architecture in the present work is no more than an elaboration upon the simple forms of buildings in the background of Roger's Baptism scene, which includes a church and a similar walled city on opposite banks of the river Jordan.

The donor represented in our painting has not been identified, but we may assume that his given name was some form of the name John (*e.g.,* Johannes, Johan, Jean, Giovanni, *etc.*). That his wife's name probably was Margaret we know from the painting which was discovered to have been joined to the same altarpiece as the inner right wing (Rochester, New York, Memorial Art Gallery), and which represents the kneeling donatrix with St. Margaret as her patron saint (cf. *Exposition Memling* [exhibition catalogue], Bruges, 1939, dealer's advertisement of F. Stern-Drey). Both wings previously have received independent attributions to Aelbert Bouts, but the current association of the works with Vrancke van der Stockt is more acceptable. Both donor panels are framed by columns of a type that appears in a series of drawings also attributed to Van der Stockt (cf. Paul Wescher, in *Old Master Drawings,* XIII, 1938-1939, p. 1 ff.). The fact that the donatrix is depicted in an interior setting facing an open doorway suggests that the missing center panel represented also an interior scene, and that it is not identical with the "Deposition from the Cross" formerly in the Demandolx-Dedon Collection, cited by Wolfgang Stechow. It is much easier to imagine the donor in a landscape setting just outside an interior than to imagine the donatrix in an interior isolated from a landscape setting. Probably the central panel depicted a Virgin and Child Enthroned, a *Sacra conversazione,* or a Throne of Mercy.

EX COLLECTION: H. Oppenheimer, London; [art market, Vienna].

EXHIBITIONS: New York, Knoedler Galleries, "Paintings and Drawings from Five Centuries," 1954, no. 21.

REFERENCES: Sale catalogue of the H. Oppenheimer Collection, London, July 24, 1936, no. 6 (as Aelbert Bouts); Max J. Friedländer, *Die altniederländische Malerei,* XIV, Leyden, 1937, p. 87; Jacques Duverger, s.v. "Stock," in Thieme-Becker *Allgemeines Künstlerlexikon,* XXXII, 1938, p. 69; Allen Memorial Art Museum *Bulletin,* XI, no. 2, Winter, 1954, no. 21, pl. 21; [Wolfgang Stechow], *Catalogue of European and American Paintings and Sculpture in the Allen Memorial Art Museum, Oberlin College,* Oberlin, Ohio, 1967, pp. 143-144, fig. 14.

Lent by the Allen Memorial Art Museum,
Oberlin College, Oberlin, Ohio,
R. T. Miller, Jr. Fund, 42.128

PLATE XLVI

28 Circle of AELBERT BOUTS, late 15th or early 16th century

*Mater Dolorosa*

The specific type of *Mater Dolorosa* exhibited here is associated with Dirc Bouts and his following as a derivation of a Dirc Bouts prototype created as a pendant to a "Man of Sorrows" (see no. 29). The original pair of votive pictures is lost, but both subjects are known through numerous copies by the workshop and following which are preserved both singly and in pairs (for the most recent list of the examples existing in pairs, see Colin Tobias Eisler, *New England Museums* [vol. 4 in *Les Primitifs Flamands,* I. Corpus de la Peinture des Anciens Pays-Bas Méridionaux au Quinzième Siècle], Brussels, 1961, pp. 59-61; for the *Mater Dolorosa* alone, see Martin Davies, *The National Gallery, London,* [vol. 3 in *Les Primitifs Flamands,* I. Corpus de la Peinture des Anciens Pays-Bas Méridionaux au Quinzième Siècle], Antwerp, 1953, pp. 35-36). The present example is stylistically related to the work of Aelbert Bouts (ca. 1460-1549), Dirc's younger son and the same artist who is responsible for the roundel version of the "Man of Sorrows" also exhibited. Instead of the stipled gold grounds of the paintings closest to the lost Dirc Bouts originals (the best versions of which are those in the Kurt Gratwohl Collection in Zürich-Erlenbach and the National Gallery in London), the presently exhibited *Mater Dolorosa* and "Man of Sorrows" have darkened backgrounds.

It is likely that works by Roger van der Weyden supplied stylistic and iconographic material for the Boutsian votive pictures and for the slightly different late fifteenth-century types known best in the pair of panels in the Groeninge Museum in Bruges (another pair in the Musée des Beaux-Arts in Strasbourg was attributed by Friedländer to Simon Marmion). But the suggestion that both sets were based on two votive paintings by Roger no longer preserved is not easily acceptable (for the Bruges paintings and this suggestion, see H. P[auwels], in *De Eeuw der Vlaamse Primitieven* [exhibition catalogue], Bruges, 1960, pp. 70-71, nos. 19-20, ill.). The iconization of Roger's spiritualized figures is a common phenomenon among the artists of the following generation who imitated his style, and the principle involved is that of creating new standard compositions with figures drawn eclectically from his works.

Oil on panel, H. 13-1/4 inches (33.8 cm.), W. 10-1/4 inches (26.0 cm.)

PLATE XLIX                                   Lent by the H. Shickman Gallery, New York

29  AELBERT BOUTS, late 15th century

*The Man of Sorrows*

Oil on panel (circular), Diam. 10-3/8 inches (26.3 cm.)

This is one of numerous examples of the "Man of Sorrows" based ultimately on a lost work by Dirc Bouts, the painter of the city of Louvain. The original, in turn, probably was derived partly from the Eyckian *vera icon* (of which the best extant version appears to be the one formerly in the Swineburne Collection in Durham), the apparent model also for the head of Christ in Dirc Bouts' *Triptych of the Last Supper* for the Church of St. Peter in Louvain. In fact, an excellent Boutsian version of the *vera icon* still exists in the Museum Boymans-Van Beuningen in Rotterdam; another is in the Museum Czartoryski in Cracow, and still others are known. The copies of the lost Dirc Bouts "Man of Sorrows" usually are of rectangular shape, sometimes with rounded top, and often are accompanied by a representation of the *Mater Dolorosa* as a pendant (see no. 28). The most recent compilation of the rectangular-shaped versions is that by Colin Eisler (*New England Museums* [vol. 4 in *Les Primitifs Flamands*, I. Corpus de la Peinture des Anciens Pays-Bas Méridionaux au Quinzième Siècle], Brussels, 1961, pp. 59-61), to which may be added the version in the Huntington Library in San Marino, California, and other examples that have appeared recently on the art market (some of which may be identical with ones already on Eisler's list). A third Boutsian type, represented by the painting in the Musée des Beaux-Arts in Dijon, shows the "Man of Sorrows" with head tilted and turned slightly to the right.

Friedländer notes the painting exhibited, one in the Museum voor Schone Kunsten in Antwerp, one formerly in the Ulrich Thieme Collection in Leipzig, and "several weak repetitions on the London art market" as circular versions of the "Man of Sorrows." The roundels, and also the tilted-head type, appear all to stem from the circle of Aelbert Bouts, the second son of Dirc (ca. 1460-1549), and are characterized by his saccharine style. The present one, the best of the known roundel versions, combines motifs from both the rectangular-type "Man of Sorrows" and the Boutsian *vera icon*. Especially the fold at the lower neck of the costume derives from the *vera icon*. The use of the roundel is also related to the idea of the *Johannesschüssel,* or plate with the severed head of St. John the Baptist, another votive image popularized by the Bouts circle. Aelbert Bouts further used the "Man of Sorrows" in triptych arrangement with the Instruments of the Passion in the wings, as the small devotional altarpiece in the collection of the New York Historical Society indicates.

The pinkness of the eyes in the earlier versions of the lost Dirc Bouts original is more strongly accentuated in the later, mostly early sixteenth century examples. The spilling teardrops that reflect light like little crystal beads become more numerous, and the face becomes more extensively dripped with blood. The green color of the crown of thorns assumes a quality of phosphoresence, and the mouth opens wider. Versions associated with Aelbert Bouts, like the present one, emphasize especially the width of the head, whereas the Dirc Bouts-type *vera icon* and "Man of Sorrows" both show elongated faces.

EX COLLECTION: Richard von Kaufmann, Berlin.

EXHIBITIONS: Lawrence, Kansas, The University of Kansas Museum of Art, "Renaissance Art," 1956.

REFERENCES: Max J. Friedländer, *Die altniederländische Malerei*, III, Leyden, 1934, p. 118, no. 62, pl. LVII.

Lent by the Nelson Gallery-Atkins Museum,<br>Kansas City, Missouri, Gift of Mrs. Mary E. Evans and<br>Mrs. John E. Wheeler in memory of Harry M. Evans, 40-44/4

PLATE XLIX

30  FLANDERS, late 15th century

*Portrait of a Young Man*

Oil on panel, H. 9-9/16 inches (24.3 cm.), W. 6-5/16 inches (16.0 cm.)

The portrait style of Roger van der Weyden was one of the most enduring expressions of Netherlandish fifteenth-century painting. Despite the major innovation of adding a window opening and view of a landscape in the background of the portrait—an achievement of Dirk Bouts' and Hugo van der Goes' time—it was Roger's somewhat aloof characterization of the sitter that still dominated the art of portraiture after his time and endured to the end of the century. Roger's pupil, Hans Memling, was much in demand as a portraitist at Bruges and left us, among numerous other portraits, the engrossing depictions of Tommaso and Maria Portinari (the donors of Hugo van der Goes' magnificent triptych for S. Maria Novella in Florence), in the style of Roger. The pair are shown against plain, dark backgrounds and with the orant hands isolated in the inside corners of the matching panels. The artist of the portrait here on exhibition was probably a contemporary of Memling and perhaps also worked in Bruges. Friedländer was nearly correct in ascribing it to the anonymous Master of the St. Ursula Legend, but the work is not by his own hand. When Charles de Tolnay gave hopes that it was an early work by Hugo van der Goes, the search for comparisons with works by the many anonymous late fifteenth-century Bruges artists was unfortunately abandoned. The portrait does, in fact, possess qualities reminiscent of Hugo van der Goes—the psychological interest, the "peculiar expressiveness" De Tolnay noticed results from the slightly asymmetrical treatment of the eyes, and the drawn cheeks. But the late Bruges and Ghent schools were virtually swept by the influence of Hugo that escaped Memling himself.

Numerous late fifteenth-century Flemish paintings, especially portraits, are preserved that neither can be associated with an important artist nor can be fitted into the stylistic reconstructions of artists whose names are unknown. For example, the "Portrait of a Man" formerly owned by Georges Wildenstein & Co. (now in an American museum) and attributed to Gerard David (cf. *Le Portrait dans les anciens Pays-Bas* [exhibition catalogue], Bruges, 1953, no. 27, fig. 30) must be removed to an "Anonymous Flemish" category, together with the present work. The portrait exhibited appears to share some characteristics of technique with a "Portrait of a Young Man" in the Accademia Carrara in Bergamo, listed among the doubtful works of Hans Memling (cf. Karl Voll, *Memling, Des Meisters Gemälde (Klassiker der Kunst)*, Stuttgart and Leipzig, 1909, ill. p. 166).

The traditional identification of this portrait as a young cleric is based on the assumption that the sitter sports a tonsure. Possibly he is slightly bald at the back of the head, but it does not appear to be a tonsure. Nor is the costume he wears the habit of any identifiable order.

EX COLLECTION: Tietje, Amsterdam; private collection, New York; [E. and A. Silberman Galleries, New York].

REFERENCES: Max J. Friedländer, *Die altniederländische Malerei*, XIV, Leyden, 1937, p. 104; Charles de Tolnay, in *Art Quarterly*, VII, 1944, pp. 184-188, 190 notes 12-14; Gordon B. Washburn, in *Museum Notes*, Museum of Art, Rhode Island School of Design, III, no. 6, 1945, pp. 1-2; Helen Comstock, in *Connoisseur*, CXVI, 1945, pp. 105-106; *Burlington Magazine*, November, 1946, p. 281; Jan-Albert Goris, *Portraits by Flemish Masters in American Collections*, Belgian Government Information Center, New York, 1949, no. 3; Erwin Panofsky, *Early Netherlandish Painting*, Cambridge, Mass., 1953, n. 332 (1); Julius S. Held, in *Art Bulletin*, XLIV, 1962, p. 346.

Lent by the Museum of Art,
Rhode Island School of Design,
Providence, Rhode Island, 45.042

PLATE XLVII

31  FRANCO-FLEMISH, early 16th century

*Portrait of Le Sieur Jérôme de Busleyden*

Oil on panel, H. 9-1/8 inches (23.2 cm.), W. 6-1/16 inches (15.4 cm.)

An anonymous artist working in the Franco-Flemish area is responsible for this portrait, which was first brought to light at the exhibition of old masters at Brussels in 1935 (World's Fair) and identified as that of Jérôme de Busleyden. Of noble family, Jérôme de Busleyden held several important religious and political posts during his lifetime (d. 1517). His family was of Luxembourg, where his father served as *prokureur-generaal* and resident member of the Council of Nobility for the Burgundian Netherlands, after first occupying the position of Secretary to the Council during the time of Charles the Bold. Educated at Louvain, Padua, Bologna, and Orléans, the younger De Busleyden was ordained a priest and thereafter served in several capacities in churches in Liège and Brabant, including that of Archdeacon at Ste. Gudule in Brussels. He preferred above all his position as Provost at Aire. With the reinstatement of the *Grote Raad,* or Grand Council, at Mechelen (Malines) in 1504, Jérôme de Busleyden was named one of the five ecclesiastical councillors by Philip the Handsome. He made several journeys on political business and died on a trip to Spain in 1517, aged about 47.

Jérôme de Busleyden was a man of letters and a respected humanist. Sir Thomas More and Erasmus of Rotterdam not only were entertained in his official residence at Mechelen but also composed verses in Latin in his honor. Of considerable interest and art historical importance is the poem among De Busleyden's collected letters and papers now in the Bibliothèque Royale in Brussels (mss. 15676-77, *Hieronimi Buslidii Carmina, Epistolae et Orationes*) which he wrote and dedicated to a triptych by the painter Hugo van der Goes (see Joseph Destrée, in *Academie royale de Belgique. Bulletins de la Classe des Beaux-Arts,* VIII, 1926, p. 26 ff). Also, we know from preserved inventories that among Jérôme de Busleyden's collection of art works and other curiosities was a painting of "The Virgin among the Sybils," supposedly the work of Hugo van der Goes. The walls of De Busleyden's palatial estate in Mechelen were decorated with frescoes of historical and mythological scenes which have been attributed to various artists, including Bernard van Orley, court painter to Margaret of Austria.

In the line of independent development of the northern portrait the present painting would seem to pose something of an anomaly. As with the portraits in the right wing of the Master of St. Ursula's diptych with the "Virgin and Child Enthroned" (Antwerp, Museum voor Schone Kunsten), the sitter presentation seems to be based on the principle of excerpting the upper half of the standard donor figure from a larger composition with religious narrative (*e.g.*, a Nativity or Adoration of the Magi). The effect is rather like that of a window frame with a screen that blocks out all but the image of the donor. The present portrait can be compared successfully with a detail of the upper body of Pierre Bladelin in Roger van der Weyden's *Bladelin Altarpiece,* the only notable fifteenth-century Netherlandish depiction of a donor in which as much attention is called to the crossing of the thumbs in the praying hands as it is here (this exceptional motif appears less noticeably in the central panel of the "Adoration of the Magi" triptych from the circle of Hugo van der Goes [Vienna, Liechtenstein Collection], Hugo van der Goes' "Portrait of a Monk" [New York, Metropolitan Museum], and in the right wing of Hans Memling's *St. Christopher Altarpiece* [Bruges, Groeninge Museum]). As it is, the arrangement iconographically calls for completion with a religious composition as the left wing, forming a diptych. The usual votive subject for such a small diptych with a donor portrait is the Virgin and Child. Although there is no indication that the present frame originally was hinged, the physical evidence, as reported by Colin Eisler, is inconclusive for establishing whether or not the frame is original. The frame has been regilded.

The arms on the painted escutcheon are definitely those of Jérôme de Busleyden, but these are not entirely trustworthy. Elza Foncke exercised some caution in accepting the portrait as that of the Mechelen patrician, and Colin Eisler has pointed out that the painting of the arms shows less precise execution than the portrait and that it covers a damaged area of the surface. Nevertheless, the present portrait seems more reliably connected with Jérôme de Busleyden than others that have been thought to represent him, including the portrait in the "Saint Jerome and a Donor" in the Johnson Collection in Philadelphia and the "Portrait of a Canon" by Quentin Metsys in the Collection of Prince Liechtenstein in Vaduz. De Vocht has considerably strengthened the identification by pointing out the similarity with the head of Daniel in the fresco depicting "Belshazzar's Feast" in the hypocaustum of De Busleyden's Mechelen residence, painted shortly after 1507. Eisler has brilliantly interpreted a passage in the Book of *Daniel* in the light of its probable appeal to the Mechelen nobleman and apparently accepts not only De Vocht's thesis that De Busleyden is represented as Daniel in the fresco, but also De Vocht's suggestion that the Queen in "Belshazzar's Feast" is a portrait of Margaret of Austria.

The "Portrait of Jérôme de Busleyden" is so much in the style of works executed in northern France that Louis Réau was inclined to attribute it to Simon Marmion, who, however, died too early (1489) for a connection of his hand with the portrait to be made plausible. Grete Ring attributed the work to an anonymous northern French artist. De Busleyden's associations with the Abbey of St. Bertin (the former location of Marmion's only fully authenticated work) through various decorative objects from there in his possession, were pointed out by De Vocht and again stressed by Eisler. Perhaps a gifted artist in the ambience of Marmion, and one who outlived the Valenciennes master by some years, can be credited with the work. Eisler is inclined to connect the commission for the portrait with the period of De Busleyden's study at Orléans and to date it in "the last years of the fifteenth century." On the other hand, Julius Held considers the evidence of costume more indicative of a date slightly after 1500. It is possible that the portrait was commissioned in 1504, when De Busleyden was appointed to the *Grote Raad*. Elza Foncke thought the costume he wears resembles the robes worn by the councillors, but De Vocht argues that a heavy gold chain which was part of their costume is absent.

EX COLLECTION: Count Kanitz, Schloss Cappenberg, Westfalen; [Lindpainter & Hinrichsen, Berlin]; Julius W. Böhler, Lucerne; Eric Lyndhurst, Brussels; [Durlacher Brothers, New York].

EXHIBITIONS: Brussels, "Cinq siècles d'Art," 1935, no. 84 (as "école de Malines, ca. 1480").

REFERENCES: *Cinq siècles d'Art. Exposition universelle et internationale de Bruxelles 1935* (exhibition catalogue), Brussels, 1935, no. 84; Elza Foncke, in *Gentsche Bijdragen tot de Kunstgeschiedenis*, V, 1938, p. 185; Wadsworth Atheneum *News Bulletin*, VI, April, 1941, no. 7; Grete Ring, *A Century of French Painting*, London, 1949, p. 222; Henry De Vocht, *Jérôme de Busleyden, His Life and Writings (Humanistica Lovaniensia* IX), Turnhout, 1950; W. Godenne and L.-Th. Maes, *Iconographie des Membres du Grand Conseil de Malines*, Brussels, 1951; Wadsworth Atheneum *Handbook*, Hartford, Conn., 1958; Colin Tobias Eisler, *New England Museums* (vol. 4 in *Les Primitifs Flamands*, I. Corpus de la Peinture des Anciens Pays-Bas Méridionaux au Quinzième Siècle), Brussels, 1961, pp. 28-32, pls. XXI-XXIV; Julius S. Held, in *The Art Bulletin*, XLIV, p. 344.

PLATE LXIX

Lent by The Wadsworth Atheneum,
Hartford, Connecticut, The Ella Gallup Sumner
and Mary Catlin Sumner Collection, 1941.155

# DRAWINGS AND PRINTS

32  JAN VAN EYCK (?), second quarter of the 15th century (?)

*St. James Minor*

Brush and pen drawing on vellum in pale, greenish-brown ink, touches of red and flesh tone, gold outlines, H. 5-1/4 inches (13.6 cm.), W. 3-3/8 inches (8.6 cm.)

Only one authenticated drawing by Jan van Eyck has been preserved: the "Portrait of Cardinal Albergati" in the Staatliche Kunstsammlungen in Dresden, dating from 1431. Among the other drawings attributed to this Bruges artist who enjoyed the patronage of the Dukes of Burgundy, this one representing the younger St. James seated and holding in his left hand a fuller's club, his attribute, holds particular interest because of the wide ramifications it suggests of the relationship between painters and sculptors during the early fifteenth century. Friedrich Winkler was the first to associate the drawing, previously attributed to Petrus Christus, with Jan van Eyck when he published a series of drawings of the twelve Apostles supposedly copied after lost originals by Van Eyck, among which the St. James Minor resembles closely the present drawing. The series, representing six standing and six seated Apostles with their names written above the figures in a Gothic hand, are in the Albertina in Vienna (cf. Otto Benesch, *Die Zeichnungen der niederländischen Schulen des XV. und XVI. Jahrhunderts [Beschreibender Katalog der Handzeichnungen in der graphischen Sammlung Albertina,* herausgegeben von A. Six, Bd. II], Vienna, 1928). Friedländer dated the originals after which the Albertina drawings were made ca. 1430, and Baldass followed with a dating between 1430 and 1434. It was Baldass' suggestion that the original drawings were used as models for small sculpted Apostles, and because of the precious rather than monumental qualities implied of the originals by the copies, he postulated that they were perhaps for the decoration of a reliquary.

Another drawing representing St. Paul, of similar measurements (5-3/4 x 3-1/8 inches, or 14.6 x 7.8 cm.) and technique to the present drawing came by way of the Paris (1927) and New York (Schaeffer Galleries, 1941) art markets into the collection of the late Robert Lehman in New York. It is also on parchment and corresponds exactly to the representation of St. Paul among the Vienna drawings, but it had the monogram of Albrecht Dürer added later. The drawings on parchment are usually considered to be finer in quality than those on paper in Vienna. That they are on parchment could possibly be interpreted as evidence of their early date. Perhaps it could even connect them with the manuscript tradition followed by Hubert and Jan van Eyck in their miniatures for the *Turin-Milan Hours,* though this point must be pursued with extreme caution. It is also possible that rather than serving as models for sculptures they were drawn *after* a series of sculpted Apostles and in fact are a primary link between the Burgundy-influenced sculpture of the early fifteenth-century Netherlands and the *grisailles* on the exterior of the *Ghent Altarpiece.*

Friedländer's and Baldass' datings for the original drawings after which the Vienna ones were copied correspond roughly with the completion date of the *Ghent Altarpiece* (1432), on the exterior of which are representations of John the Baptist and John the Evangelist simulating unpainted, sculpted figures. The Vienna drawing depicting St. John the Evangelist is actually rather close to the interpretation of the same figure on the *Ghent Altarpiece* wings. Further, there is a striking similarity in the treatment of drapery between an alabaster figure here attributed to the workshop of the Master of Rimini (no. 56) and the drawing of St. James Minor. Carmen Gómez-Moreno (*Medieval Art from Private Collections* [exhibition catalogue], New York, 1968, nos. 47-48) has already suggested that the Vienna drawings are the link between the *Ghent Altarpiece* and figures which she published from the school of the Rimini Master; however, she sees the *grisaille* figures as influencing, by way of the Eyckian drawings, sculpted figures rather than the reverse, as is suggested here. In any event, it should be pointed out that the lines of drapery in the alabaster figure are sharper than those in the drawing of St. James Minor, and in turn, the lines of drapery in the present drawing are sharper and more angular than in the corresponding drawing in Vienna.

EX COLLECTION: William Russell; Charles Fairfax Murray, London.

EXHIBITIONS: New York Public Library, 1919; Iowa City, State University of Iowa, "Six Centuries of Master Drawings," 1951, no. 4; Detroit Institute of Arts, "Masterpieces of Flemish Art: Van Eyck to Bosch," 1960, no. 67; Bruges, "De Eeuw der Vlaamse Primitieven," 1960, no. 70.

REFERENCES: *J. Pierpont Morgan Collection of Drawings by the Old Masters formed by C. Fairfax Murray* (catalogue), London, 1905-1912, I, no. 225; Friedrich Winkler, in *Jahrbuch der königlich preussischen Kunstsammlungen,* 1916, p. 297, n. 2; Max J. Friedländer, *Die altniederländische Malerei,* I, Berlin, 1924, p. 126, n.; Otto Benesch, *Die Zeichnungen der niederländischen Schulen des XV. und XVI. Jahrhunderts* (*Beschreibender Katalog der Handzeichnungen in der graphischen Sammlung Albertina,* herausgegeben von A. Six, Bd. II), Vienna, 1928, p. 1, under no. 7; Ludwig Baldass, *Jan van Eyck,* London-New York, 1952, p. 284; *Six Centuries of Master Drawings* (exhibition catalogue), Iowa City, 1951, no. 4; *Flanders in the Fifteenth Century* (exhibition catalogue), Detroit, 1960, pp. 227-228, no. 67, ill.; *De Eeuw der Vlaamse Primitieven* (exhibition catalogue), Bruges, 1960, pp. 172-173, no. 70; Max J. Friedländer, *The Van Eycks—Petrus Christus,* Leyden-Brussels, 1967, p. 74, n. 12, pl. 68 D.

Lent by The Pierpont Morgan Library, New York, Cat. I, no. 225

PLATE XXIV

33  ROBERT CAMPIN (?), ca. 1430-1440

*The Bad Thief on the Cross*

Silverpoint drawing on paper prepared with tan-grey ground, H. 10-1/4 inches (26.1 cm.), W. 5-1/2 inches (14.0 cm.)

This magnificent drawing can be connected with Robert Campin's *Descent from the Cross Triptych* (ca. 1430) as the most reliable extant transmittal of the thief on the cross from the left wing. Of Campin's original work, only a fragment of the right wing with the other thief, the converted Roman Centurion, and another Roman soldier, has been preserved (Frankfurt, Staedelsches Kunstinstitut). The entire composition, however, including the *grisaille* wing exteriors, is known through the slavish and inadequate copy in the Walker Art Gallery in Liverpool, England (cf. Erwin Panofsky, *Early Netherlandish Painting,* Cambridge, Mass., 1953, pp. 167-168, 423-424, notes 167 [1], 168 [1]). In addition, the two thieves, the Centurion, and the swooning Virgin supported by St. John are reflected, but interpreted more freely, in the *Passion Altarpiece* by the Bruges artist known as the Master of 1500 (cf. Hélène Demoriane, in *Connaissance des arts,* No. 208, June, 1969, pp. 72-79).

The drawing is far superior to any of the painted copies of the thief in the left wing and actually was published by Jakob Rosenberg as an original study by Campin for his altarpiece. But as Panofsky has pointed out, there are signs in the drawing of a concern for the parts over that for the whole; and like most fifteenth-century Flemish drawings that have been preserved, this surely was executed after the painting. Haverkamp-Begemann implies that it is characteristic enough of Campin to be thought a work from his own hand; one might well consider that once the altarpiece was finished Campin executed the drawing himself as a model for his students.

The problem of the drawing's formal relationship to the lost triptych by Campin is relatively uncomplicated in comparison to that of its iconographic interpretation. Ever since Theodor Musper wrote about the surviving fragment of Campin's altarpiece, in Frankfurt (*Untersuchungen zu Rogier van der Weyden und Jan van Eyck,* Stuttgart, 1948, p. 26), it has been disputed as to which of the two thieves, the good or the bad, the Frankfurt painting represents, and consequently which is intended in the present drawing. In the most recent study on Campin (Mojmir Frinta, *The Genius of Robert Campin,* London, 1966), the question is left open. Panofsky wanted to agree with Musper that the Frankfurt thief is the Good Thief (and hence the thief in the lost left wing reflected in our drawing is the Bad Thief), but he could not bring himself to imagine any other than the Good Thief to the right of Christ and in the same wing with the donor. But to Panofsky's description of the Frankfurt thief, which seems to argue against his own pronouncement on its iconography (". . . while the figure of the Bad Thief is normally distinguished by violence of movement and coarseness of type, it here appears so perfect in structure and modeling and so tragically beautiful in movement and expression that it almost seems to defy the limitations of the Gothic style") may be added the argument that the blindfolding parallels the symbolism of Synagogue blindfolded in contrasting pairs of Ecclesia and Synagogue (such as the famous sculptures at Strasbourg Cathedral). The blindfolding would seem to mark the left thief, the one in the drawing, as the Bad Thief, the unenlightened; at the same time, the Centurion seems appropriately inspired beneath the Good Thief in the Frankfurt painting. Ironically, an eclectic painter of ca. 1500 who has been called both Spanish and Netherlandish transferred the thief in the present drawing to Christ's left side (in reverse) in a painting now in the Museum Naradowe at Poznań, at the same time forgetting the symbolism of the blindfold and providing both thieves with blindfolds (cf. Jan Bialostocki, *Malarstwo Niderlandzkie Wzbiorach Polskich, 1450-1500* [exhibition catalogue], Warsaw, 1960, pp. 82-84, no. 57, fig. 61).

EX COLLECTION: [H. M. Calmann, London].

EXHIBITIONS: Philadelphia Museum of Art, "Masterpieces of Drawing," 1950-1951, no. 6; Newark Museum, "Old Master Drawings," 1960, no. 3; Cambridge, Massachusetts, Busch-Reisinger Museum, "Northern Renaissance Exhibition," 1967.

REFERENCES: *Masterpieces of Drawing* (exhibition catalogue), Philadelphia Museum of Art, 1950, no. 6, ill.; *Old Master Drawings* (exhibition catalogue), Newark, New Jersey, 1960, no. 3, ill.; Jakob Rosenberg, in *Art Quarterly*, Summer, 1950, pp. 250-251, ill.; Erwin Panofsky, *Early Netherlandish Painting*, Cambridge, Mass., 1953, I, p. 423, n. 167 (1); Egbert Haverkamp-Begemann, in *Great Drawings of All Time*, edited by Ira Moskowitz, New York, 1962, p. 454.

PLATE XXVIII
Lent by the Fogg Art Museum, Harvard University, Grace Nicholas Strong and Alpheus Hyatt Funds

34  Follower of ROGER VAN DER WEYDEN, ca. 1445

*Men Shovelling Chairs*

Pen and ink on paper, H. 11-3/4 inches (30.0 cm.), W. 16-3/4 inches (42.6 cm.)

Late Medieval painters not only were employed to paint sculptures; they also supplied sculptors with designs. This drawing is a unique surviving example of such designs for sculpture and obviously is created for a curved surface. On style it can be associated with a distinguished follower of Roger van der Weyden, the great City Painter of Brussels.

That the drawing was produced in Brussels is confirmed by a sculpted capital of nearly identical design preserved in the Musée Communal de Bruxelles. The connection with the very weathered capital from the exterior arcade of the Brussels Town Hall was first seen in the drawing by W. J. Fulton (in a letter to the late Robert Lehman dated March 11, 1952) and again, independently, by Jean Adhémar and L. Lebeer. Prior to this, Erwin Panofsky had interpreted the meaning of the drawing's curious subject from Flemish proverbs, according to which the piling of chairs (symbols of the privileged class of society) and stools (symbols of the lower classes) implies social upheaval (reported by Agnes Mongan). Thus, Adhémar was reminded that one of the participants in a popular insurrection in Brussels in 1421 was Jan Van Ruysbroeck, the architect commissioned in 1448 to construct the tower of the Brussels Town Hall. However, it is unlikely that the capital for which the present drawing is the original design alludes to any specific social disorder; it is even more unlikely that Jan van Ruysbroeck had any connection with the sculptures or produced designs in the style of Roger van der Weyden. However, Lebeer's suggestion that the capital may commemorate a house with the sign of the "Scupstoel," which formerly stood on the Town Hall site, is quite valid. The name combines the words "schup," meaning "shovel" as well as "kick," and "stoel," meaning "chair" or "stool." Haverkamp-Begemann notes that even today "op de schoepstoel zitten" in Dutch means "be likely to get kicked out" and that the capital's presence on the Town Hall façade may have served secondarily to remind the city officials that they were subject to being kicked out.

EXHIBITIONS: Cambridge, Massachusetts, Fogg Museum of Art, "Seventy Master Drawings," 1948; Philadelphia Museum of Art, "Masterpieces of Drawing," 1950-1951, no. 16; Brussels, "Bruxelles au XV^e siècle," 1953, no. 1; New York, The Metropolitan Museum of Art (Cloisters), "Medieval Art from Private Collections," 1968-1969, no. 20.

REFERENCES: Agnes Mongan, *One Hundred Master Drawings*, 1949, no. 8, pl. 9; *Art News*, November, 1950, p. 24; *Masterpieces of Drawing* (exhibition catalogue), Philadelphia, 1950, no. 16, ill.; Jean Adhémar, in *Bulletin de la Société des Antiquaires de France*, 1952-1953, p. 142 (letter of March 18, 1953); L. Lebeer, in *Bruxelles au XV^e siècle* (exhibition catalogue), Brussels, 1953, pp. 193-195, ill.; Carmen Gómez-Moreno, *Medieval Art from Private Collections* (exhibition catalogue), New York, 1968, no. 20, ill.

PLATE XXIX
Lent by The Lehman Collection, New York

35  BURGUNDY (?), third quarter of the 15th century

*Studies of Two Male Figures*

Pen and ink, H. 7-11/16 inches (19.5 cm.), W. 3-9/16 inches (9.0 cm.)

These drawings, one on each side of the sheet, both represent heavily robed, standing male figures, one facing to the right and the other to the left. The more finely drawn figure, who faces right and gestures with his left hand, also holds a letter or document in his right hand and directs his eyes toward the spectator. When it was sold in Berlin in 1930 the drawing was thought to be perhaps a pair of studies for a Pilate and a Pharisee (for an *Ecce Homo* composition), but they could just as easily be studies for or after a painted Crucifixion, or figures forming part of a secular composition (cf. the miniature representing "The Princes of the World Proceeding to the Court of the Emperor in Constantinople" in the *Fleur des Histoires* manuscript exhibited here, no. 11, which shows similar gesticulating figures). The sheet has been trimmed on all four sides, as evidenced by the way parts of each figure have been cut off at the margin.

The present drawing was first attributed to Hugo van der Goes, and later to an anonymous Netherlandish fifteenth-century master. The first attribution can be ruled out entirely, and for the second there is too little similarity in technique to the small number of surviving fifteenth-century Netherlandish drawings to uphold a Netherlandish origin. At best there is only a superficial similarity to drawings associated with Vrancke van der Stockt. On the French side, any association with a figure like Simon Marmion would be unlikely, because Marmion's only drawing considered authograph (the *Pietà* in the Fogg Museum, Cambridge) is entirely Flemish in technique. If only by process of elimination, one can best imagine an origin in Burgundy for our drawing. The Burgundian costume, the strong part played by the drapery in each figure, and especially the portrait-like treatment of the face of the figure standing to the right, could thereby be explained. Until now, the only feasible attribution of a fifteenth-century drawing to Burgundy has been the famous "Standing Ecclesiastic with Folded Hands" in the Boymans Museum in Rotterdam, also often attributed to the Master of the Aix Annunciation (cf. [Agnes Mongan], in *Great Drawings of All Time,* edited by Ira Moskowitz, III, New York, 1962, no. 641).

EX COLLECTION: C P S (Lugt 622); J. D. Böhm; Licht.

REFERENCES: Sale catalogue of the Böhm Collection, Vienna, 1865, no. 1291; *Eine Wiener Sammlung. Erste Teil. Alte Handzeichnungen* (sale catalogue of C. G. Boerner, Leipzig, and Paul Graupe, Berlin), 1930, p. 6, no. 23, pl. ix.

PLATE XXXIII                    Lent by The Lehman Collection, New York

36  FLANDERS (?), 15th century

*Head of a Monk*

Silverpoint drawing on white paper, H. 2-15/16 inches (7.6 cm.), W. 2-3/8 inches (6.0 cm.)

This "Head of a Monk" may not represent an ordinary monk at all, but rather the head of St. Gregory from a Mass of St. Gregory (cf. the standard composition represented by the left wing of a triptych by the Master of the St. Catherine Legend in the Mauritshuis in The Hague [Max J. Friedländer, *Die altnieder-ländische Malerei,* IV, Berlin, 1926, no. 54a] and by a panel from a series formerly associated with Jan van Eyck, but dating from the second half of the fifteenth century, in the Metropolitan Museum of Art in New York [H. B. Wehle and M.

Salinger, *The Metropolitan Museum of Art. A Catalogue of Early Flemish, Dutch and German Paintings*, New York, 1947, no. 21.134.3B]. The possibility of a profile portrait is extremely unlikely for the fifteenth century—and there should be no doubt that this is a fifteenth-century drawing—but the uplifted eyes and the slightly tilted-back position of the head establish a link with compositions of the Mass of St. Gregory, in many of which Gregory's head appears in profile.

We therefore are concerned here with what is probably a fragment of a drawing, or at least a drawn detail of a larger, probably painted composition. The drawing style is that which we today understand (on fragmentary evidence) as of Roger van der Weyden and his followers, and there is a strong possibility that the work dates no later than around the middle of the fifteenth century. The most reliable parts of the faint drawing (it seems to have been extensively retraced at a later date) reveal a technique of shading with long, parallel curvilinear strokes that is characteristic of the most reputable drawings of similar date. Almost no cross-hatching occurs along the collar, where one would most expect it in a later drawing.

EX COLLECTION: Charles A. Loeser; Paul J. Sachs.

REFERENCES: Elizabeth Mongan and Paul J. Sachs, *Drawings in the Fogg Museum of Art*, Cambridge, 1940, no. 458, fig. 232.

PLATE XLVI

Lent by the Fogg Art Museum, Harvard University, Bequest of Meta and Paul J. Sachs

37   FLANDERS, ca. 1470-1480

*The Bear Hunt*

Pen and sepia on paper, H. 11-3/4 inches (29.9 cm.), W. 16-3/4 inches (42.6 cm.)

Very likely a project for festive decorations lies behind this drawing representing a "Bear Hunt." The flattening-out of the landscape crowded with figures, the high horizon, and the circular development of the composition around the principal motif of the bear attacked by dogs suggest a connection with a tapestry or wall painting, either as the design for or the reflection of a larger scale work. In some respects it is the stylistic successor to Hugo van der Goes' lost composition, "David and Abigael," which presumably is transmitted in part by the drawing representing "The Meeting of Jacob and Rachel," preserved in Christ Church, Oxford (cf. Egbert Haverkamp-Begemann, in *Great Drawings of All Time*, edited by Ira Moskowitz, New York, 1962, II, no. 466). In others, it is the predecessor to the series of tapestries known as *The Hunt of the Unicorn* (New York, Metropolitan Museum of Art), probably ordered in celebration of the marriage of Louis XII and Anne of Brittany in 1499 (see James Rorimer, in Metropolitan Museum of Art *Bulletin*, n.s., I, Summer, 1942, p. 11).

A fine webbing of lines and the tendency to work up the detail in one area at a time (here primarily at the left) describe the working pattern of the artist of this drawing. Perhaps we are confronted here with the drawing style of Hugo van der Goes in the hands of a miniaturist, which exactly describes a stylistically similar *grisaille* miniature included in this exhibition (no. 23). The connecton with the manuscript miniature is supported by a comparison of the head of a man seen immediately below the man and woman riding horseback in the left-hand corner of the drawing with the head of the man receiving the book in the manuscript dedication miniature. Parallels in technique between the miniature and drawing are also to be noted.

The inscription on the reverse of the drawing, reading *FRANÇOIS A BECKE*, may date as early as the sixteenth century and probably observes a traditional attribution, if indeed it does not copy an earlier signature. But an artist with this name is not known to us presently. Following an attempt to ascribe the drawing to the monastic artist Jan Beeck of Liège (*Master Drawings* [exhibition catalogue], Buffalo, 1935, no. 10), the discovery was made that among the painters who contributed to the designs for decorations for the marriage celebration of Charles the Bold and Margaret of York in 1468 were a Jehan and a Jos van der Beecke (*La Collection Lehman* [exhibition catalogue], Paris, 1957, no. 110). The geographic proximity to Ghent or Bruges suggested by the stylistic evidence of the *grisaille* miniature mentioned above would further enhance the argument that the author of the present drawing was related to the two Van der Beeckes, Jehan and Jos.

The past confusion of the drawing's subject matter with a scene of boar hunting is not without significance, for the representation is a member of a tradition that began with the December calendar page representing a boar hunt in the manuscript known as the *Très Riches Heures,* produced ca. 1409-1416 by the Limbourg brothers for the Duc de Berry (Musée de Chantilly). A more literal rendering of the Limbourg brothers' famous composition was made in a place far removed from the present drawing's place of origin—in fact, in Austria —but at a time not much later—in 1507—among Rueland Frueauf the Younger's series of Flanders-inspired landscapes for Archduke Leopold.

EX COLLECTION: Mrs. Chauncey J. Blair, Chicago.

EXHIBITIONS: Albright Art Gallery, Buffalo, "Master Drawings Selected from the Museums and Private Collections of America," 1935, no. 10; Paris, Musée de l'Orangerie, "La Collection Lehman de New York," 1957, no. 110; Cincinnati Art Museum, "The Lehman Collection," 1959, no. 283.

REFERENCES: *Master Drawings* (exhibition catalogue), Buffalo, 1935, no. 10, ill.; Grace Frank and Dorothy Miner, *Proverbes en Rimes,* Baltimore, 1937, p. 24; *La Collection Lehman de New York* (exhibition catalogue), Paris, 1957, no. 110, pl. LIV; *The Lehman Collection, New York* (exhibition catalogue), Cincinnati, 1959, p. 27, no. 238, ill.

PLATE LXXV                                            Lent by The Lehman Collection, New York

38    FRANCE, ca. 1500

*A Lady with Three Suitors*

Pen and brown ink and ink wash on paper, H. 9-1/16 inches (23.0 cm.), W. 7-5/8 inches (19.4 cm.)

The woman seated at the left and encircled by a chain on the ground is presenting her three suitors with a challenge to their ardent pursuits. The arrangement with the chaste maiden within an enclosure is reminiscent of the tapestry known as the "Unicorn in Captivity," probably ordered in 1514 by Francis I to add to the famous series called the *Hunt of the Unicorn,* made for Anne of Brittany in celebration of her marriage to Louis XII in 1499. In 1514 Francis married Anne's daughter. The Unicorn, while there represented as the Risen Christ, was also a time honored symbol of chastity. The slightly suggestive play on visual symbols in the drawing is repeated in the inscription written above, which reads: *Celui mamour conquestera/ qui deca ce lass passera/ sanss lempirer ne desnourer/ sans dessuss/ ne dessoubz passer.*

It is possible that this is a design for a tapestry or an embroidered pillowcase that also would have borne the four-line passage, and that because of this, the artist has left most of the background to the tapestry weaver's imagination. Or is it, perhaps, a drawing made after a tapestry whose composition and inscription struck the fancy of the artist? This would explain the artist's apparent need for at least a ground line and for shadows cast by the figures and objects. The maiden is shown wearing the Breton headdress that Anne of Brittany had made popular in the French court when she married Charles VIII (d. 1498), but the headdress was also popular during her second reign as the wife of Louis XII. The drawing therefore could conceivably date after the turn of the sixteenth century. Wixom cites the presence of a watermark of a wheel which is similar to a known example that was used within the period 1484-1525.

EX COLLECTION: Moscardo, Verona (Lugt 2990 b-h); Marchese of Calceolari.

EXHIBITIONS: Cleveland Museum of Art, "Treasures from Medieval France," 1966-1967, no. VII-11.

REFERENCES: William Wixom, *Treasures from Medieval France*, Cleveland, 1967, pp. 314-315, no. VII-11, ill.

Lent by The Cleveland Museum of Art,
John L. Severance Fund, 56.40

PLATE LXVIII

39  MASTER W⚹, ca. 1465-1485

*A Ship Steering to the Right* (Lehrs 38)

Engraving, H. 6-7/16 inches (16.4 cm.), W. 4-1/4 inches (11.7 cm.)

The engraver known as the "Master W with the Key," after the initial *W* and the key-like device found on many of his printed engravings, is especially notable among early printmakers because he seems to have been the only one directly connected with the Burgundian court. Localized on technical evidence of his prints to Bruges, where he would have been active from the late 1460's to the early 1480's, the artist must have worked for Charles the Bold. The Master W's engraved coat-of-arms of the Burgundian Duke, of which the only known copy was discovered among the Burgundian manuscripts and documents in the Bibliothèque Royale in Brussels late in the nineteenth century, could be assigned a date between 1467 and 1472 on evidence in the heraldry. The most absorbing works of the artist, though not the technically most refined, are those representing the Burgundian army encampments. Hollstein (*Dutch and Flemish Etchings, Engravings and Woodcuts*, Amsterdam, XII, n. d., p. 218) accepted an early date for them by associating them with Philip the Good of Burgundy; Lehrs (*Geschichte und kritischer Katalog des deutschen, niederländischen und französischen Kupferstichs im XV. Jahrhundert*, Vienna, VII, 1930, pp. 5, 23) rightly subscribed to the interpretation of them as made after observations in the field during the Burgundian War of 1473 or the storming of Neuss in 1475. Connected with these, too, are the various engravings of rows of Charles the Bold's cavalry and foot soldiers. There is nothing remotely like them before the seventeenth century.

The engraving of a ship displayed here is one of eight different sailing ships and warships engraved by the Master W with the Key that have survived. Some of them exist in only one impression, and it is likely that others besides the eight are lost; the present example is one of three known impressions of the same engraving. These are the only known individual engravings of ships from the fifteenth century, and as such, are primary documents for naval history. Lehrs had at first thought that these ships must represent members of Charles the Bold's fleet of vessels so important to his ambitions (*Der Meister W ⚹, ein Kupferstecher der Zeit Karls des Kühnen*, Dresden, 1895, nos. 30-37); however, he retracted this view later after reading Huizinga's description of the way Charles'

44

ships were lavishly fitted and after consulting a naval expert. He admitted that only one of the ships (L. 41), the only one labeled *kraeck*, represented a man-of-war, and even this lacked the arms of Charles the Bold. Lehrs concluded that the series of ships had been created for use as models for painters, woodcutters and miniaturists and, on the information of Wolfgang Boerner (*Der Meister W* ⚒ [inaugural dissertation], Bonn, 1927), was able to document their actual use in the Nürnberg woodcut-illustrated *Schatzbehalter* of 1491 and *Liber Chronaricum* of Hartman Schedel of 1493.

Several years ago an interesting pen drawing of a ship appeared on the art market and was thought to be a study by the Master W with the Key for one of his ship engravings (see catalogue no. 33 of the dealer William H. Schab, New York, 1962, p. 158, no. 153). Admittedly, the drawing has some connection with the master, but the claim that the streamers bear the Burgundian lion as Charles the Bold's emblem and therefore make up for the lack of an emblem on any of the ship engravings is irreconcilable with the evidence in the drawing. The emblems on the two streamers are distinctly those of a winged lion and a ram; the draughtsmanship is much cruder than that displayed by the Master W with the Key in his engravings and lacks the spontaneity of his battle encampment scenes and ships. The drawing is probably by a German artist who copied one of the master's ship engravings, now lost, and might better be used to explain the appearance of the Netherlandish artist's ships in German woodcuts.

PLATE XXXV

Lent by The Art Institute of Chicago, The Potter Palmer Collection

40  MASTER F V B, active ca. 1475-1500

*The Judgment of Solomon* (Lehrs VII.116.2 [I])

Engraving, H. 10-1/4 inches (26.1 cm.), W. 8-5/8 inches (22.0 cm.)

The sheer brilliance in technique of the Netherlandish engraver known as the Master F V B suggests that he learned the art of engraving in a leading goldsmith's shop. He is perhaps the only Netherlandish engraver to have achieved excellence on a par with the great fifteenth-century German engravers like Schongauer, and it is true that he was strongly influenced by Schongauer. A highly developed realism and a spiritual kinship with Netherlandish painters, including Dirc Bouts and Hans Memling, distinguish his production (see Max Lehrs, in *Print Collector's Quarterly*, X, 1923, pp. 3-30). Because of its size, composition, and technique, the "Judgment of Solomon" is usually considered his best work. However, it is relatively early among his works and must have been executed before 1488, when it was copied in a woodcut illustration to Johannes de Thwrocz's *Chronica Hungarorum*, published in Augsburg. It probably dates between 1480 and 1485.

The engraving illustrates a popular story of King Solomon's justice concerning a dispute between two women over the possession of a child. Solomon has just passed the decision to have the child literally divided between the two, and the executioner, doffing his cap like the third magus in Roger van der Weyden's famous *Columba Altarpiece*, is starting to draw his sword at the order of the courtier standing in front of him. The groupings of figures are the most successful of the artist's career. Two of the figures stand with their backs to the spectator, closing the space around the young Solomon. The exquisite ornaments on the throne and the fine brocade behind Solomon recall one of the Master F V B's best engravings of pure ornament.

Lent by The Metropolitan Museum of Art, New York, Gift of Felix M. Warburg and his Family, 41.1.41

PLATE XL

41    MASTER I A M of ZWOLLE, active ca. 1475-1504

*The Skeleton in the Tomb*  (Hollstein XII.276 [different state])

Engraving, H. 13-1/8 inches  (33.3 cm.), W. 8-7/8 inches  (22.6 cm.)

The anonymous North Netherlandish engraver who often added the weaver's shuttle device to his monogram and the name *zwott*, for "Zwolle," on his prints produced the most painting-like compositions of any fifteenth-century engraver. His technique is hard and a little monotonous by late fifteenth-century standards, and the medium of engraving seems to have served him as a way to reproduce painted compositions rather than as the means of developing his own idiom of the print. "The Skeleton in the Tomb" is least like his other engravings in that it appears less outspokenly eclectic. The theme is an elaborately developed allegory on transitory life and the ultimacy of death. Skulls depicted as reminders of death are quite common during the fifteenth century and even appeared on the reverse of painted portraits; this is an unusually gruesome *memonto mori* emphasizing the decay of viscera and the horrifying presence of a toad and a serpent, symbols of evil.

The Master I A M of Zwolle apparently was in Gouda and Delft around 1475 but centered most of his activity in Zwolle, the city of his birth. His engravings show him aware of the South Netherlandish painters, especially Roger van der Weyden.

Lent by The Metropolitan Museum of Art, New York, The Elisha Whittelsey Fund, 59.595.23

# SCULPTURE

42    FRANCE OR FLANDERS, 14th century

*A Knight*

Black stone of Tournai, H. 14-1/8 inches  (36.0 cm.)

A black stone quarried in large quantities around Tournai in the Hainaut was a favored material for tomb sculpture during the Later Middle Ages. It was exported to England and used widely for tombs there. This figure of a knight probably was carved on the Continent and may have decorated the lower part of a tomb. In spite of the damaged condition of this fragment of a relief, one can see that the sculptor is interested in the specific realism of the belt tightening against the hip as a result of the weight of the sword on the opposite side. He relieves the strict frontal pose slightly by raising the right arm across the chest in a relaxed gesture signifying honor, and by uplifting the face and turning it toward the raised right shoulder. Both idealism and realism combine in the face.

EX COLLECTION:  Engel-Gros, Paris; Henry Walters, Baltimore.

EXHIBITIONS:  Norfolk Museum of Arts and Sciences, "Life in the Gothic Age," 1955.

REFERENCES:  Paul Ganz, *Catalogue Raisonné de la Collection Engel-Gros*, Paris [1925], I, p. 94, no. 1; II, pl. 42a.

PLATE III

Lent by The Walters Art Gallery, Baltimore, 27.266

43  FRANCE, 14th century

*Head of a Man: arm-rest from a choirstall*

Walnut, H. 14-7/16 inches (36.7 cm.), W. 5-7/16 inches (13.9 cm.)

Lent by The Walters Art Gallery, Baltimore, 64.2

44  FRANCO-FLEMISH, ca. 1375

*Madonna*

Marble, H. 19 inches (48.2 cm.), D. 3-3/4 inches (9.5 cm.)

This standing figure has been associated with the art of the Meuse valley and may come from the city or the region of Liège. The material is a white marble of a type and quality found in the area of Liège, and other figures carved from it are known. The proportions of the figure, the bulk and weight of the drapery, and to an extent the facial features, are actually more realistic than those of the "Virgin and Child" in the Lille Museum, a sculpture with which this figure has been compared (for the Lille Virgin and other works stylistically related to it, see William H. Forsyth, in *Metropolitan Museum Journal*, I, 1968, pp. 41-59). However, the stylization of the hair, buckling "L"-shaped folds of drapery at the base of the figure, and exposure of the forms of the feet beneath the drapery find parallels in other Mosan sculptures. The stereotyped facial expression relates the figure to works made in France during the time of Charles V, when there was a strong new wave of Italian influence.

The very high relief of the figure makes it appear almost free-standing, and indeed it is a self-contained unit with a backing that has been finished roughly along the sides. It probably was made to fit into a multi-figured arrangement, perhaps in a niche. The grimacing face and the stance suggest that it is the Virgin beneath the cross on Calvary. Perhaps the group, which would have been completed with a mourning St. John on the right and a Crucified Christ on a cross raised on a mound of earth in the center, was set into the wall of a niche framed at the top by an arch.

EX COLLECTION: Dr. Hugo Oelze, Amsterdam; [Edward R. Lubin, New York].

PLATE VIII

The University of Kansas Museum of Art,
Gift in Memory of Mary Morrill Litchfield
by Members of her Family, 69.35

45  FLANDERS, early 15th century

*Head of Christ*

Polychromed wood, H. 11 inches (28.0 cm.)

Little known even among scholars of Late Gothic art, this head of Christ from the *corpus* of a wooden crucifix is one of the few remnants of Flemish sculpture still left to represent the International Style. It is but a late survivor—a ghost— of a sculptural tradition that sent a number of great South Netherlandish artists, mostly painters, to the courtly circles in France before 1400, filled with the concern for plastic modelling. The head is said to have come from Oost-Cappel near Hondschoote, twenty-nine miles from present-day Dunkerque and very near the border of Belgium. Though the area is part of France, it then belonged to the cultural realm of Flanders. Not many miles west and just a little south, in the Artois, was born Jacquemart de Hesdin, the manuscript illuminator whose activity in

Paris during the last two decades of the fourteenth century brought a new progressive stage to the development of spatial interest and plasticity. Panofsky has remarked that the present sculpture "gives the impression of a head of Christ by Jacquemart de Hesdin enlarged and transposed into a three-dimensional medium." The formula might easily be reversed.

If an entire life-size figure of Christ suffused with the beauty of this head can be imagined, it will be seen that this is a precious beauty on a large scale, not a beauty resulting from monumentality. Panofsky stresses this difference in appreciating the style of the sculptor Claus Sluter, whose smaller sculptures, no less than his large ones, have monumental values. In the delicately modelled head of Christ reposes an actual strength in beauty of plastic form. It is interesting to compare it with the Christ figure in the painted miniature from a Flemish Missal (no. 4), which, like Jacques de Baerze's *corpus* (Art Institute of Chicago) from his carved altarpiece for the Chartreuse de Champmol near Dijon (1391), is less idealized and also less magnificent. In its noble humanization of Christ our head compares more closely with that in the "Crucifixion with the Martyrdom of St. Denis" by Jean Malouel (completed after 1416 by Henri Bellechose). One wishes that the rest of the body remained to compare with the painted work of Malouel, who also came from the North.

The stylization of the beard in our head of Christ and the carefully polychromed surface are part of that preciousness which is made to retreat by the persuasive realism of the parted lips, the prominent cheek bones, and the heavy eyelids. The success of the combination is a tribute to the International Style, the conqueror of Europe around 1400.

PROVENANCE: Church of Oost-Cappel, near Hondschoote.

EXHIBITIONS: The John Herron Art Institute, Indianapolis, "Masterworks of Sculpture," 1956.

REFERENCES: *Catalogue of the Paintings and Sculptures in the Permanent Collection,* Albright Art Gallery, Buffalo, 1949, p. 213, no. 230; *Fortune,* December, 1945, p. 141, ill.; Erwin Panofsky, *Early Netherlandish Painting,* Cambridge, Mass., 1953, p. 80, n. 80 (6).

PLATE XI

Lent by the Albright-Knox Art Gallery, Buffalo, New York, James G. Forsyth Fund

46    FRANCO-FLEMISH, early 15th century

*Prophet*

Marble, H. 13-1/4 inches (31.2 cm.)

Of André Beauneveu's sculptural decorations from after 1395 for the Duc de Berry's Sainte-Chapelle built next to his residence at Bourges, we are left with but three fragments of Apostles' heads plus five small figures of Prophets of unequal finesse in carving from his workshop. In the marble figure included here is clearly to be seen the reflection of Beauneveu's and his assistants' Sainte-Chapelle figures, although it is a work of an artist less skilled than even Beauneveu's immediate assistants. Overlooking the inexpressive hands and the inadequate scroll, one can find much to recommend this figure in terms of its documenting Beauneveu's profound influence around 1400. The style of the beard and the structure of the mouth and chin are actually closer to one of the fragmentary Apostle heads by Beauneveu than is any of the five remaining Prophet figures from his workshop (cf. Theodor Müller, *Sculpture in the Netherlands, Germany, France, and Spain, 1400-1500,* Harmondsworth, 1966, fig. 23A). The style of drapery which clings rather tightly to the body, but which produces loose, tubular folds that often run parallel, can be found in some of the small Beauneveu workshop Prophets from Bourges (cf. Georg Troescher, *Die burgundische Plastik des ausgehenden Mittelalters,* Frankfurt, 1940, figs. 14, 15), as can the motif of exposing the form of the foot beneath the drapery (*Ibid.,* fig. 12).

The small size of this sculpture and the fact that it is executed in marble suggest that it was perhaps intended to serve as decoration for an altar in a church. Small traces of paint on the surface indicate that it was originally polychromed and partly gilded.

REFERENCES: *Smith College Museum of Art* (catalogue), Northampton, Mass., 1938, p. 32.

Lent by The Smith College Museum of Art,<br/>Northampton, Massachusetts

PLATE XV

47  FRANCE, early 15th century

*Three fragments from an altar retable or tabernacle: clustered column; relief with Prophet; Crucified Christ*

Alabaster; Column, H. 14-3/4 inches (37.5 cm.); Prophet, H. 6-1/8 inches (15.6 cm.); Christ, H. 10-5/8 inches (27.0 cm.)

The ultimate provenance of these three pieces, obviously fragments of a more extensive sculptural work, is unknown. They have been unpublished since 1920 when they quietly entered the Metropolitan Museum, where they are considered as possibly related to a Saint Denis group of sculptures. In style they are vaguely reminiscent of the products of workshops following the tradition of André Beauneveu, whose activity was centered in Bourges. The relief Prophet is especially instructive, for in this figure the series of long, straight vertical folds that lend support to the upper part of the body are present alongside a piece of hanging drapery with an elaborate curvilinear motif. The idealized Christ figure, with the crown of thorns treated in a regularized manner and the face and body carved smoothly, relaxes from the awesome conception witnessed in the also fragmentary Christ figure from Claus Sluter's *Well of Moses,* with which one would judge it is nearly contemporary.

The work to which these fragments belonged may have been produced in the Ile-de-France, as has been suggested, or they may have come from one of the outlying Burgundian centers, such as Vienne. However, the flatness of the figures and the drapery style in the Prophet are reminiscent of the statue of about 1405 supposedly representing Louis de Châtillon from the Sainte-Chapelle at Bourges (cf. Joan Evans, *Art in Medieval France,* London, 1948, fig. 183b). Nor does the *corpus* compare unfavorably with the well known relief of the "Man of Sorrows" now in the Museum at Bourges (cf. Theodor Müller, *Sculpture in the Netherlands, Germany, France, and Spain, 1400-1500,* Harmondsworth, 1966, pl. 25B).

The most challenging problem connected with these fragments is that of imagining how they were placed as components in the original work, which must have comprised small architectural elements with relief decoration as well as figure sculptures. Any reconstruction must be based on the one surviving clustered column, which on one side has a square shaft without a foliate capital and a pin at the top for attaching a springing element. This could lessen the possibility that the columns were placed in a single row. One can imagine a zig-zag arrangement of alternating square piers and clustered columns connected at the top by arches, as is found on Sluter's *Tomb of Philip the Bold,* and with the Prophet figures placed on top of the outer-most piers like the tiny angels on the *Tomb of John the Fearless*. But such a design would not easily explain a use for the Crucified Christ. However, if one imagines four clustered columns placed in the corners of a square with their square shafts turned inward, it will be seen that the Prophets can form decorations on the outside corners above the clustered columns, leaving room for arches to spring between the four columns. The open space framed by columns on all four sides still does not allow enough room for the Christ figure—it must originally have measured about 16 inches (40.6 cm.), taller with the cross—but by filling in an imaginary screen of open tracery between the Prophets and the point of the arch on all four sides, one completes a squared-off top upon which a Crucified Christ on a square platform can be lifted. Such an arrangement could serve only one purpose: to house the Holy Sacrament on the high altar. Iconographically, it would relate directly to Claus Sluter's *Well of Moses* at the Chartreuse de Champmol near Dijon, in which the Prophets who announce the imminent death of Christ form a socle upon which the cross is raised. The theme would be ideally suited to the display of the sacrament below, the *sangue Christi*.

EX COLLECTION: J. G. Demotte, New York.

REFERENCES: Metropolitan Museum of Art *Bulletin,* XV, 1920, p. 235.

PLATE XIV

Lent by The Metropolitan Museum of Art, Gift of J. G. Demotte, 20.58.3, 4, 5

48  FRANCE (Franco-Flemish?), early 15th century

*Head of an Angel*

Marble, H. 5 inches (12.7 cm.), W. 5-1/2 inches (14.0 cm.), D. 4-1/2 inches (11.4 cm.)

The origin of this marble head remains a puzzling problem, as there is a lack of stylistically similar examples with which to compare it. Verdier is correct in citing as related a marble angel in high relief in the Morgan Collection of the Metropolitan Museum (cf. [Georg Swarzenski], *Arts of the Middle Ages* [exhibition catalogue], Boston, 1940). This, it would seem, is more likely to be dated around 1400 than to the traditionally accepted "last decades of the fourteenth century." Less convincing is Verdier's comparison of the head with the angel in a pair of marble reliefs representing the "Annunciation" in the Julius Böhler Collection in Munich (cf. *Europäische Kunst um 1400* [exhibition catalogue], Vienna, 1962, no. 431, p. 324, ill. 66-67, as "Flemish (?), early 15th century"). The latter could easily have been produced in North Italy, whereas the simple incising for the eyelids in the present example is decidedly of French or Franco-Flemish experience. A limestone figure of an angel of about 1430 in the Los Angeles County Museum of Art (where it is dated 14th century) displays an identical rendering of the hair in spiraling locks and a similar treatment of the eyes, while it also shows in the figure and drapery the influence of Sluterian art and in the lyre-shaped face points toward the later alabaster reliefs from a roundel formerly together in the Chauncey J. Blair Collection in Chicago and included in this exhibition (nos. 59, 60). It is possible that all the examples mentioned, with the exception of the Böhler reliefs, are northern French works that range in production over a long period, but the problem of the angel head probably will never really be solved until the matching body is found.

EX COLLECTION: R. Heim, Paris; [Jacques Seligmann & Co., New York].

EXHIBITIONS: Baltimore, Walters Art Gallery, "The International Style," 1962, no. 88.

REFERENCES: [Philippe Verdier], in *The International Style* (exhibition catalogue), 1962, p. 88, no. 88, pl. LXXVIII.

PLATE XV                                    Lent by John Goelet, New York

49  BURGUNDY (School of Dijon), second quarter of the 15th century

*Pleurant*

Marble, H. 14 inches (35.6 cm), W. 5-1/4 inches (13.3 cm.), D. 3-1/2 inches (8.9 cm.)

When Philip the Bold, the Valois Duke of Burgundy, founded the Carthusian monastery at Champmol near Dijon in 1383, it was with the intent of providing a place where he and his successors eventually could be interred in ducal splendor. He engaged the sculptor Jean de Marville to erect his tomb; but when the artist died in 1389, having barely begun the project, the task fell to the Netherlandish talent Claus Sluter. Sluter created for the Burgundian Duke a sepulchral monument of revolutionary concept and ingenious design in which the base supporting the *gisant,* or reclining portrait effigy, is processed around by numerous Carthusian monks in mourning. This, however, is not the essence of Sluter's innovation; earlier tombs in France and the Netherlands had reserved this part of the tomb for such funeral processions. Rather, it was Sluter's contribution to see in a traditional arrangement the possibilities for representing a specific sorrow for a specific event in a group of figures that move freely in an open arrangement and benefit from a realistic and vital three-dimensional interpretation. The mourning Carthusian monks, known as *pleurants,* are conceived as individual statements of weeping and sorrow in a context of more general mourning.

Sluter, who did not live to see the tomb completed (it was finished by his assistant and nephew, Claus de Werve), initiated a Burgundian tradition for tombs decorated with characteristic free-standing *pleurants.* The arrangement was immediately adopted for the tomb of Philip the Bold's successor, Duke John the Fearless (d. 1419), begun by Claus de Werve and finally completed in 1470 by Antoine le Moiturier. *Pleurants* by Étienne Bobillet and Paul de Mosselman adorned the tomb of Philip the Bold's brother Jean, Duc de Berry (completed ca. 1453). Charles I de Bourbon specified the Champmol tomb of Philip the Bold as a model to be followed when he drew up a contract for his tomb with the sculptor Jacques Morel at Lyon in 1448. Many of these Burgundian tombs were severely damaged during the French Revolution, including those of Philip the Bold and John the Fearless, or lost some of their figures which have since turned up in private collections and public museums; others were completely destroyed.

The *pleurant* figure here exhibited comes from an as yet unidentified tomb in Burgundy and probably dates from the second quarter of the fifteenth century. The monk, heavily draped in the simple habit of the Carthusian Order and holding rosary beads in his left hand, is shown lifting back his cowl with a raised right arm (now missing). In so doing, he exposes a face ridden with grief, eyes gazing into space, mouth drooping at the corners. While the rich yellow-marble material of the present figure sets it apart from usual Burgundian ones of vizille alabaster, there is an immediacy to its relationship with the figures from the tomb of Philip the Bold that distinguishes it from other *pleurants* produced during the second half of the century. In fact, the figure is modelled directly upon one of the *pleurants* from the Philip the Bold tomb, a sculpture now in the Musée de Cluny in Paris (cf. Georg Troescher, *Die burgundische Plastik des ausgehenden Mittelalters,* Frankfurt, 1940, II, pl. LXI, fig. 243). Documents exist for Burgundian tombs adorned with *pleurants* for which there is no remaining evidence *in situ.* For example, it is known that the Spaniard Juan de la Huerta, who was engaged to complete the tomb of John the Fearless and his wife, Margaret of Bavaria, after the death of Claus de Werve in 1439, previously was commissioned by Louis, Comte de Châlon-Arnay, to execute three family tombs with mourning figures at Mont-Ste.-Marie in the province of Doubs (see D. Roggen, in *Gazette des Beaux-Arts*, XVI, 1955-1956, p. 151). The tombs were completely destroyed during the French Revolution; but there is always the possibility that single figures from these, or from other documented but also destroyed tombs, have survived.

EX COLLECTION: S. W. Straus, New York.

EXHIBITIONS: New York, Jacques Seligmann & Co., "Loan Exhibition of Religious Art," March, 1927.

REFERENCES: *Loan Exhibition of Religious Art* (exhibition catalogue), New York, 1927.

PLATE XXII                                                                          Lent anonymously

50  BURGUNDY (School of Dijon), second quarter of the 15th century

*St. Thecla*

Limestone, H. 24 inches (60.9 cm.)

Claus Sluter, in the service of Philip the Bold, Duke of Burgundy, revolutionized French sculpture with his figures of unprecedented monumentality generated by a vital and powerful realism. Upon his death in 1405/1406 Sluter left not only a productive workshop but also a capable assistant to lead it, Claus de Werve. Sluter's work at Champmol and the products of his Dijon-situated workshop, influenced sculpture in many parts of Europe and provided a legacy upon which Burgundian sculpture could draw for yet another generation to come. The School of Dijon which he had founded continued to be active beyond the middle of the century, while until at least 1450 sculptural decoration with figures inspired by Sluter's and Claus de Werve's works near Dijon kept appearing in churches in all parts of Burgundy. The St. Thecla included here is related to the Dijon workshop and may have been produced there during the second quarter of the fifteenth century. The sculptures produced in various parts of Burgundy in Sluter's following all have in common the amplitude of drapery, but the differences between the several lines of development lie in the way the drapery relates to the figure beneath.

This sculpture representing the first-century saint whose undying admiration for St. Paul caused her to be tortured by various means, including fire and beasts (hence the attributes she carries), probably owes its immediate inspiration to the master from Sluter's workshop who sculpted both a Mary Magdalen now in the Museé Rolin in Autun and the well known Detroit Virgin (cf. [Philippe Verdier], in *The International Style* [exhibition catalogue], Baltimore, 1962, pp. 79-80, no. 79). But if the Detroit Virgin, executed about 1425-1430, "abandons [the] inner force and power" of Sluter's style (William Wixom, *Treasures from Medieval France* [exhibition catalogue], Cleveland, 1967, p. 254), then our St. Thecla may be said to abandon the Detroit Virgin's remarkably human countenance and to supplant whatever is left of Sluter's personal style in its drapery arrangement with a garment that can only be described as performing like rolled-out pastry dough. The closest stylistic parallel for this and for the treatment of the facial features can be found in a Virgin and Child preserved in the Town

Hall in Dijon (cf. Georg Troescher, *Die burgundische Plastik des ausgehenden Mittelalters,* Frankfurt, 1940, II, fig. 275).

PLATE XXIII

51  FRANCE (?), second half of the 15th century

*St. John the Baptist*

Limestone, H. 26 inches (66.0 cm.)

The impact of Claus Sluter's sculptural achievements in Burgundy around 1400 was so far-reaching in Europe that it is often difficult to localize lesser works which show Burgundian influence. This St. John the Baptist fits an iconographic type of St. John, with the figure heavily draped but the right leg exposed, and with the Lamb resting on the open book held in the figure's left hand, that was made popular in Burgundy. It is the type documented in the large sculpture from Poligny which is in the Metropolitan Museum in New York (26.63.27; cf. James J. Rorimer, in Metropolitan Museum of Art *Bulletin,* IX, 1951, p. 183), yet it does not possess the abundant drapery which streams from the arms downward on both sides and which displays long folds in successive loops across the front. The heavily wrinkled face is more reminiscent of the Burgundian St. John figures that show a lineal descent from the Zacharias on Sluter's *Well of Moses,* like the one in the Pierpont Morgan Library in New York (cf. [Philippe Verdier], in *The International Style* [exhibition catalogue], Baltimore, 1962, pp. 85-86, no. 83). However, it is enough removed from the immediacy of the Burgundian experience, both temporally and geographically, to warrant the suggestion that the present St. John the Baptist was made in some other area—for example, Provence. In spite of its greater utilization of stylized locks of hair to the sides and back, this sculpture's head shows a striking similarity to one of the heads preserved in the Musée Calvet in Avignon (cf. Georg Troescher, *Die burgundische Plastik des ausgehenden Mittelalters,* Frankfurt, 1940, II, pl. XVI, no. 152). An origin in Provence might help explain how the figure found its way to Spain, where it was discovered by its present owner.

EX COLLECTION: [Linares, Madrid].

Lent anonymously

52  BRABANT, ca. 1410

*Apostle*

Boxwood, H. 12-3/4 inches (32.5 cm.)

This figure is one of the rare surviving examples of early fifteenth-century Flemish wood sculpture. It is a product of the International Style, which is epitomized in Italy in the Apostle sculptures by Jacobello and Pierpaolo dalle Masegne for the choirscreen of St. Mark's in Venice, and in France by the sculptures of Claus Sluter. In fact, there is evident in this figure something of an Italianate quality that is less pronounced in the *Hakendover Altarpiece,* to which it is related (cf. *Flanders in the Fifteenth Century* [exhibition catalogue], Detroit, 1960, pp. 231-234, nos. 69-70, ill.). The boxwood material lends the figure a precious quality, and yet it is powerfully conceived. In spite of its material and small scale, it gives a monumental impression of a figure cast in bronze. The bold sweep of drapery lines radiating from beneath the hidden right forearm, and the realism concentrated in the face, place the figure at a critical moment of the development of Northern art.

Jaap Leeuwenberg (in a letter to a former owner dated May 26, 1967) related the present figure to the statuettes on the retable of the Reinoldi-Kirche in Dortmund (cf. *Wallraf-Richartz Jahrbuch,* XXVII, 1965, figs. 67, 113), and to an Apostle figure in the Rijksmuseum in Amsterdam (cf. Irmingard Geisler, in *Wallraf-Richartz Jahrbuch,* XVIII, 1956); however, these are more distantly related than the *Hakendover Altarpiece,* which probably was produced in Brussels. In addition, the walnut Apostle figures in this exhibition (nos. 54, 55), associated here with the Rijksmuseum sculpture mentioned above, should be mentioned in connection with this boxwood figure.

To imagine the original setting for this figure one must reject any notion that it was originally part of a large, complex work. Boxwood is rarely encountered used for a figure as large as this, and it is hard to imagine this usage being extended to a large number of figures in the same work. It is easier to imagine it as a principal part of a relatively portable mounting.

EXHIBITIONS: New York, "Art Treasures Exhibition," 1967; Florence, Italy, "V. Biennale, Mostra Mercato Internazionale dell'Antiquariato," 1967.

PLATE XXI                    Lent by Gordon A. Pfeiffer, Wilmington, Delaware

53  NETHERLANDS (Guelders?), early 15th century

*St. Christopher*

Lindenwood with traces of polychromy, H. 30-3/4 inches (78.1 cm.)

This sculpture came to its present collection, where it is ascribed to Burgundy or West Germany (ca. 1390), only about ten years ago as a gift without a provenance. While the thick legs and style of drapery and beard at first suggest an origin in the northern provinces at a date when the primitive realism of that area influenced more southern developments, the realism in the faces and especially the structure of the heads is too developed to uphold a late fourteenth-century dating. In fixing its probable place of origin, one is tempted to place it in one of the provincial areas northeast of the County of Flanders, in one of the borderline zones susceptible to influences from various regions. The face of St. Christopher seems already to bear the impression of Burgundian developments around the turn of the century, while the smiling Christ Child seems almost to foreshadow the playful infants of Nicolaus Gerhaerts, who was born in Leyden in the North Netherlands. In drapery style the sculpture relates to the art of Brabant, specifically to the well known group of "Christ Carrying the Cross" in the Musée de Cluny in Paris (cf. Theodor Müller, *Sculpture in the Netherlands, Germany, France, and Spain, 1400-1500,* Harmondsworth, 1966, pl. 15A) and the two walnut Apostle figures included in this exhibition (nos. 54, 55). One of the regions capable of producing such hybrid forms would be Guelders, situated between the ecclesiastical principality of Liège and the County of Cleves, and between Brabant and Germany. Though not controlled by the Duchy of Burgundy, it was one of those areas that politically and culturally came under Burgundy's influence.

REFERENCES: *European Works of Art in the M. H. de Young Memorial Museum,* San Francisco, 1966, ill. p. (32).

Lent by the M. H. de Young Memorial Museum,
PLATE XX                    San Francisco, Gift of Mr. and Mrs. Ralph C. Lee, 59.32

NETHERLANDS, early 15th century

54    *Apostle*

Walnut, H. 17-5/16 inches  (44.0 cm.)

55    *Apostle*

Walnut, H. 17-1/2 inches  (44.4 cm.)

These two Apostle figures, along with two more from the same series, came to the University of Kansas collections (acc. nos. 66.1-4) as "French, Burgundian, early fifteenth century." In all likelihood they originally had formed part of a carved altarpiece in which the Apostles were placed in pairs turned slightly in toward one another. Philippe Verdier (in a letter dated April 23, 1968) related the four figures to the Apostles from the *Altar of the Passion* in the Reinoldi-Kirche in Dortmund, calling them German, mid-fifteenth century (cf. *Wallraf-Richartz Jahrbuch,* XXVII, 1965, figs. 67, 113).

Not only are the Kansas Apostle figures more indicative of a Netherlandish tradition—one which nevertheless shows contact with the art of Claus Sluter—but also the retable in the Reinoldi-Kirche itself is clearly related to Netherlandish examples like the *Altarpiece of the Miraculous Foundation* of the Church of Saint-Sauveur in Hakendover (cf. Irmingard Geisler, in *Wallraf-Richartz Jahrbuch,* XVIII, 1956; *Flanders in the Fifteenth Century* [exhibition catalogue], Detroit, 1960, pp. 231-234, nos. 69-70, ill.). It is now apparent that a Netherlandish Apostle figure of walnut sold to the Rijksmuseum in Amsterdam in 1949 as from the *Hakendover Altarpiece* (Inv. no. RBK 16119; Geisler, *op. cit.,* p. 148) is closely related to the figures shown here, and in fact, belongs to the same Apostle series. Further, another figure in the D. Hannema collection at Heino, Holland (cf. D. Hannema, *Kunst in Oude Sfeer,* 1952, p. 74, fig. 50), and two more now in an unidentified collection in South America already have been associated with the Rijksmuseum figure as components of the same altarpiece (I am indebted to Dr. W. Halsema-Kubes of the Rijksmuseum for this information). In all, then, eight Apostle figures which belonged together originally are now known, and it is conceivable that there were no more than this. Perhaps a larger Blessing Christ figure was mounted in the center of this altarpiece, which must have been produced in the same ambience as, but is not identical with the *Hakendover Altarpiece.*

The Rijksmuseum Apostle (H. 39.5 cm.) is somewhat shorter than any of the Kansas examples; but of the four no two are of the same height. The Rijksmuseum piece shows some traces of original polychromy, and from this it can be postulated that the entire set of Apostle figures originally was painted. Further related is the boxwood statue of an Apostle included in this exhibition (no. 52), which probably is of slightly earlier date and shows greater simplicity of form and a smaller proportion of head to body.

EX COLLECTION:  Garbaty, Berlin; Nicholas de Koningsberg, New York; [Blumka Gallery, New York].

PLATE XXI                    The University of Kansas Museum of Art, 66.1, 2

56  NORTHERN FRANCE or the NETHERLANDS, second quarter of the 15th century

*St. Peter*

Alabaster, H. 21 inches  (53.3 cm.)

It is difficult to fix the place of origin of this sculpture. Stylistically it bears closest resemblance to a group of sculptures from the workshop of the Master of Rimini, named after his retable from a monastery church near Rimini in Italy, of which the figures are now preserved in the Staedelsches Kunstinstitut in Frankfurt. The Rimini Master, whose origin is to be sought in the art of northern France and the Netherlands in the early fifteenth century, seems to have wandered to the middle Rhine region between about 1420 and 1430, and subsequently to northern Italy about 1440. The earmarks of his style, present in the example shown here, are high cheek bones and sunken cheeks, protruding eyeballs set behind sharply delineated eyelids, and stringy hair executed in parallel incised lines. Frequently, as here, the sculptures of his school show the influence of Claus Sluter and the Burgundian school of sculpture. Particularly in the broad folds and simple lines of functional drapery this influence is felt.

This St. Peter has previously been directly connected with the School of Dijon and its founder, Claus Sluter. Stanley Ferber sees in it the tradition of the *pleurants* from Sluter's *Tomb of Philip the Bold,* completed in 1406, but finds an even closer parallel in a small alabaster figure of St. Benedict in the Museum Boymans-van Beuningen in Rotterdam, dated ca. 1420. But in none of the Burgundian sculptures do we find the broad planes and angular features of the face, nor the flat, rectangular forms of drapery. Rather, one is reminded of the "Head of St. John the Baptist" in the Bayrisches Nationalmuseum in Munich (cf. Theodor Müller, *Sculpture in the Netherlands, Germany, France, and Spain, 1400-1500,* Harmondsworth, 1966, pl. 73A), or even the later Apostle figures attributed, like the Munich head, to the school of the Master of Rimini and now divided among various private collections (cf. Carmen Gómez-Moreno, *Medieval Art from Private Collections* [exhibition catalogue], New York, 1968, nos. 47-51).

EXHIBITIONS: Binghamton, New York, State University of New York, University Art Gallery, "Developments in the Early Renaissance," 1968, no. 26.

REFERENCES: S[tanley] F[erber], in *Developments in the Early Renaissance* (exhibition catalogue), Binghamton, New York, p. 32, no. 26.

PLATE XXIV                                         Lent by the Paul Drey Gallery, New York

57   FRANCE, 15th century

*Corpus from a Crucifix*

Polychromed wood, H. 9-1/2 inches (24.1 cm.), W. 2 inches (5.0 cm.), D. 1-1/2 inches (3.8 cm.)

Although this small, armless *corpus* from a Crucifix affords some comparisons with early fifteenth century works like the Flemish-style head of Christ on exhibition (no. 45) or the fragmentary alabaster *corpus* (no. 47), the treatment of the loincloth and the modelling of the legs and thighs indicate that it belongs to the same period as the French paintings influenced by the work of the Flemish painter Roger van der Weyden (not before 1450-1455). The long heart-shape of the head and the sunken cheeks denote a French response to the spiritualizing aesthetic represented best by the Northern painter's work. The hair and the features of the face are carved with extreme delicacy, and the suggestion of anatomical structure is subtly conveyed in the torso. A smooth-rubbed polychrome finish adds to the intimate appeal of this object.

PLATE LII                                                                   Lent anonymously

*Musical angels*

Alabaster, partly gilded and polychromed, H. 8 inches (20.3 cm.)

These three musical angels, of which one plays a portable organ and another strums a lute, form a triangular relief which thematically is reminiscent of the two panels in the upper storey of the Van Eyck *Ghent Altarpiece*. A first impression of this fine white-alabaster, delicately-gilded group in high relief is that it is precious, early, and believably "Burgundian" (under which label it is displayed in its home collection). The expressions of the faces are easily mistaken for realism, and the evidence of the drapery is at best inconclusive. Only together with its companion-pieces is the correct picture brought into focus. The two additional groups of winged angels exhibited here (nos. 59, 60) originally formed the lower half of a roundel to which the present relief also belonged in the upper right. The missing fourth quarter is said to be in an unidentified European museum. The three reliefs exhibited were together in the same collection until 1939. Apparently at some time the present segment was shortened by perhaps as much as three inches in order to make it rest flat; the resultant loss of lower drapery and shortening of the figure proportions have previously affected the interpretation of the style. But the lower segments of the roundel—or, rather, oval—indicate that the place of origin is northern France and that the group is to be dated in the period of the so-called *détente* style. Especially the region of Champagne during the late fifteenth and early sixteenth century favored the *détente* style, which renounced Burgundian realism for a proto-Renaissance idealism. In a sense it was a return to the humanistic idealism of the thirteenth century. Seen in the context of the other groups, the relief with three musical angels still puts a strain on the terms "idealism" and "realism." The gestures of the hands, for example, are realistic, but their smoothly-modelled, wax-like forms are born of idealism. In a certain respect the group is the successor to an idealistic phase of the International Style of around 1400 (see no. 48).

EX COLLECTION: Comte de Montbrizon, Château de Roch, France; Chauncey J. Blair, Chicago; [French & Co., New York]; Joseph Brummer, New York.

EXHIBITIONS: Château de Bagatelle; Art Institute of Chicago; Buffalo Museum of Art; Cleveland Museum of Art, 1916; Mt. Holyoke College, Massachusetts, "The Eye Listens," 1950; Lyman Allyn Museum, New London, Connecticut, 1959.

REFERENCES: Sale catalogue of the Joseph Brummer Collection at Parke-Bernet, New York, May 11-14, 1949, p. 145, no. 585; Ellen Gutsche, unpublished paper submitted for course work, Yale University, 1952.

Lent by the Yale University Art Gallery,
New Haven, Connecticut,
PLATE LV
Maitland F. Griggs, B.A. 1896, Fund, 1949.99

NORTHERN FRANCE, last quarter of the 15th century

59  *Winged Angels*

60  *Winged Angels*

Alabaster, H. 11 inches (28.0 cm.) [each group]

These two reliefs of three angels each, together forming half of an oval, originally were placed as units in the same multi-relief arrangement with the group of three musical angels displayed above (no. 58) and a fourth relief which is now in a European collection. The figures in the present two reliefs display only traces of the gilding that is so well preserved in the other segment. The relief with the three musical angels also provides the evidence that the background was originally painted a deep green, and perhaps partly brown. The banderoles held by each of the lower groups originally bore inscriptions in gold that have disappeared, with the exception of a few letters. Evidently, the oval-shaped grouping formed the central part of an altar retable for which Ellen Gutsche found an iconographic parallel: a roundel from a church in Troyes (Champagne) which is now in the Louvre (cf. Michele Beaulieu, in *Description raisonnée des sculptures du Moyen-Age, de la Renaissance, et des temps modernes, Musée National du Louvre,* edited by Marcel Aubert, Paris, 1950, I, no. 393; see also Raymond Koechlin and J. J. Marquet de Vasselot, *La Sculpture à Troyes et dans la Champagne méridionale au seizième siècle,* Paris, 1900, p. 148). The reliefs, in the *détente* style, can be only partly explained by Troyes and the Champagne. Perhaps they were executed in some other part of northern France that had contacts with the Champagne region. There are indications that the artist used somewhat remote prototypes for his figures (see no. 48).

CONDITION: The left wing of one of the angels in the left group mended, damage to the scrolls in both groups.

EX COLLECTION: Count de Montbrizon, Château de Roch, France; Chauncey J. Blair, Chicago; [French & Co., New York].

REFERENCES: Ellen Gutsche, unpublished paper submitted for course work, Yale University, 1952.

PLATE LV

Lent by The Galleries, Cranbrook Academy of Art, Bloomfield, Michigan

61  CENTRAL FRANCE, mid-15th century

*St. Crispin*

Limestone, H. 38-1/2 inches (97.8 cm.)

Both the style and iconography of this figure argue for its placement in the central region of France. Although the resemblance Valentiner noted to a head of an Apostle from Mehun-sur-Yèvre, attributed to Jean de Cambrai and now in the Louvre, can only be regarded as superficial, the fact remains that other sculptures displaying this particular head type, with elongated shape, high cheek bones, and long hair framing the face, show a provenance from the region around Bourges (cf. a head supposedly from the small set of Prophet figures of the Cathedral of Notre-Dame-la-Blanche in Bourges, reproduced in Georg Troescher, *Die burgundische Plastik des ausgehenden Mittelalters,* Frankfurt, 1940, fig. 21). Even assuming that this sculpture was produced three or four decades after the completion of the sculptural decoration for Mehun-sur-Yèvre, this is still very early for a tableau-like conception in a sculptural work such as we have here. St. Crispin, the patron saint of shoemakers, is shown cutting a piece of leather, while below on a shelf of his work table are displayed a finished pair of shoes and other implements of his trade. The known examples of single figures of St. Crispin are French and number very few. A late fifteenth-century wooden example representing a man cutting leather on a workbench, probably St. Crispin, was formerly in the Octave Homberg Collection (cf. Joan Evans, *Life in Medieval*

*France,* London, 1957, fig. 52). Our figure was very likely commissioned for a church by the local guild of shoemakers.

EX COLLECTION: William Randolph Hearst.

EXHIBITIONS: Claremont, California, Scripps College, "Scripps Christmas Exhibit," 1952.

REFERENCES: W. R. Valentiner, *Gothic and Renaissance Sculptures in the Collection of the Los Angeles County Museum,* Los Angeles, 1951, no. 19, p. 56.

PLATE LVI             Lent by the Los Angeles County Museum of Art, 49.9.15

62    FRANCE, mid-15th century

*St. George*

Limestone, H. 15 inches (38.1 cm.), W. 15-1/2 inches (39.3 cm.)

The figure of which this is a fragment must have adorned an important church portal or shrine in northwestern France. It is said to have come from Caen in Normandy. The renewal of artistic endeavors during the fifteenth century in the area of Normandy dates from the time when the Duke of Bedford moved from Paris and established residence in Rouen, probably bringing with him a host of artisans. Also, the Cathedral of Saint-Maclou at Rouen was begun in 1432. The present sculpture reveals relationships with mid-fifteenth century works of Lorraine and the Bourbonais, particularly in the fleshiness of the face. The stylization of the hair and the simplicity of the drapery are extremely misleading for dating the piece; the treatment of the chain-mail and the area around the neck are more reliable points of departure for the dating. The same aesthetic for simple, rounded form of the head is seen in the head of Louis XI from Toul in Lorraine, dating from the third quarter of the fifteenth century (Art Institute of Chicago; cf. Meyric R. Rogers and Oswald Goetz, *Handbook to the Lucy Maud Buckingham Medieval Collection,* The Art Institute of Chicago, 1945, p. 63, no. 13, pls. XX-XXI). The chain-mail and raised right arm indicate that this is St. George, defender of the Church. He probably would have held a shield in his left hand, while resting his left foot on the dragon and piercing the creature with a long spear held in his raised right hand. Traces of polychromy remain on the surface.

REFERENCES: Nelson Gallery of Art *Handbook,* edited by Ross E. Taggart, Kansas City, 1959, p. 53, ill.

PLATE LIV            Lent by the Nelson Gallery of Art-Atkins Museum, Kansas City, Missouri, 35-18

63    FLANDERS, ca. 1475

*Relief with Two Angels Holding Symbols of the Passion*

Oak, H. 25-1/2 inches (54.8 cm.)

Apparently this was the left wing or section of a small altarpiece representing either the "Throne of Mercy" or the "Man of Sorrows." Another pair of angels with further Instruments of the Passion would have completed the ensemble at the far right. Perhaps the artist was active in one of the artistic centers of Flanders such as Ghent or Bruges, through which there was much trade and export to other parts of Europe. The dealer who formerly owned this piece was able to discover definite stylistic relationships with a stone relief representing the "Investiture of St. Ildefonso" in the Cathedral of Córdoba, Spain (cf. Georg

Weise, *Spanische Plastik aus sieben Jahrhunderten,* Reutlingen, 1925, pl. 124). It would not be necessary to suppose that the workshop was actually located in that region, for the export of works from Flanders to Spain was very heavy during the fifteenth century.

Especially characteristic of this master's style is the wig-like hair, seen particularly in the right figure. His figures are elongated and are covered by drapery that crumples about the waist and falls from the shoulders in slashing lines, breaking into sharp folds at the bottom of the figure. The heavy cheeks of the left angel are found similarly in a kneeling figure at the left in the Córdoba relief. The present relief probably was originally polychromed, and perhaps partly gilded, although the polychromy which has been removed since it was in the Louis Mohl collection was a more modern one.

EX COLLECTION: Louis Mohl, Paris; Le Barbier de Tinan, Paris; [Edward R. Lubin, New York].

REFERENCES: *Catalogue des bois sculptes . . . composant la collection de feu m. Louis Mohl,* Paris, May, 1912, p. 19, no. 71, ill.

PLATE XLIII

Lent by the Andrew Dickson White Museum,
Cornell University, Ithaca, New York

64   FLANDERS, late 15th century

*St. Bavo*

Oak, H. 45-1/2 inches  (1.14 m.)

So many magnificent Flemish paintings remain from the period of Roger van der Weyden, Hugo van der Goes, and their followers that it is easy to forget the important role sculpture must have played in late fifteenth-century Flanders. This impressive wood figure representing St. Bavo, patron saint of the city of Ghent, invalidates any theory that places Flemish sculpture in a minor category. An elongation of the figure, long lines of drapery, and a cylindrical-shaped head are elements of abstraction that are offset by the finely executed realistic detail of leather straps, armor fittings, and chain-mail. One can easily imagine a setting for this figure in a great hall in late fifteenth-century Flanders.

PLATE XLVIII

Lent anonymously

65   FRANCO-FLEMISH, 15th century

*Grotesque Figure: arm-rest from a choirstall*

Oak, H. 8-1/2 inches  (21.6 cm.)

This amusing carved figure probably decorated the arm-rest of a choirstall. Girded by bands that come across the shoulders, cross the chest and back, and follow the waist, the gowned and hooded old man holding his head with both hands appears introspective and perhaps slightly deranged. He belongs to the repertory of beggars, invalids, and the physically or mentally abnormal who often serve as elements of genre in the religious scenes of Late Gothic art (cf. the beggar in "St. George Baptizing the Pagan King," no. 67). Analogies with this particular example have been recognized in the choirstall figures of the Church of St. Sulpice in Favière, Seine-et-Oise (cf. Paul Vitry and F. Brière, *Documents de sculpture française,* Paris, 1904-1911, pl. 133, nos. 7, 10).

EX COLLECTION: Georges Hoentschel.

REFERENCES: A. Pérate and Gaston Brière, *Collections Georges Hoentschel . . . I, Moyen-âge et renaissance*, Paris, 1908, p. 14, pl. III; Joseph Breck, *Catalogue of . . . Sculpture*, Metropolitan Museum of Art, New York, 1913, no. 184.

PLATE LXI

Lent by The Metropolitan Museum of Art,
Gift of J. Pierpont Morgan, 16.32.292

## 66  SOUTH NETHERLANDS, late 15th century

*The Entombment of Christ*

Polychromed oak, H. 14-1/2 inches (36.9 cm.), W. 17 inches (43.2 cm.), D. 4-1/2 inches (11.4 cm.)

Most of the important documented works of late fifteenth- and early sixteenth-century Brabantine (or otherwise South Netherlandish) sculpture have been either destroyed or subjected to severe alteration and restoration. Few figural groups that survive from the large altarpieces, the glories of Netherlandish Late Gothic church decoration, are of the quality and remarkable state of preservation that can be seen in this "Entombment of Christ." The excellently preserved original polychromy allows one to see that the sculptors derived their color schemes, like their compositions, from the works of painters. At the same time, there is to be sensed in the work an adherence to a local sculptural tradition evidenced by the way in which the sculptor relates solid forms to one another (cf., for example, the "Entombment of Christ" in the Mrs. Jacob M. Kaplan Collection, ill. in Carmen Gómez-Moreno, *Medieval Art from Private Collections* [exhibition catalogue], New York, 1968, no. 45 [where it is dated in the first third of the fifteenth century, perhaps too early; "middle," or even "second third" would be more acceptable]). Here the vivid colors used in the figures surrounding the body of Christ contrast the pale color of Christ's flesh. The painting works hand in hand with the modelling to produce the desired effects of realistic appearance and emotion. Perhaps the most noteworthy personal expression of the artist is to be seen in the Magdalen, who gazes in disbelief at the gaping wound.

PLATE LX

Lent anonymously

## 67  BRABANT, late 15th or early 16th century

*St. George Baptizing the Pagan King*

Oak, H. 20-1/2 inches (52.0 cm.), W. 17-1/2 inches (44.4 cm.)

Although this handsome carved wood relief has no apparent connection with the art of Jan Borman (active ca. 1479-1520), to whose workshop it previously has been attributed, it is representative of the fine-quality wood sculptures produced in the large workshops in North and South Brabant around 1500. It represents one of the many episodes from the life of St. George in which the second-century saint converted pagans to Christianity, and it must have formed part of a large carved altarpiece that represented many scenes from his life. Of the two leading centers which produced large carved altarpieces—Antwerp and Brussels—the latter seems the more likely place of origin, yet the sculpture is not engraved with the hallmark of Brussels. The genre interest in the crippled beggar at the lower left and the contrast between the serene expression in the face of St. George and the expressions of wonderment or disturbance in most of the other faces add enormously to the appeal of the ceremonial narrative. A fine sense for variety in textures and a rendering of lavish detail distinguish the execution.

EX COLLECTION: [Blumka Gallery, New York].

61

REFERENCES: University of Kansas Museum of Art *Handbook*, Lawrence, 1962, p. 33; Marilyn Stokstad, *The Medieval Collections of The Museum of Art,* University of Kansas, Lawrence, 1963, no. 17, p. 11, ill. p. 3.

PLATE LXI

The University of Kansas Museum of Art,
Gift of Mr. and Mrs. Simon Hurwitz, 54.118

68 UTRECHT, early 16th century

*Madonna and Child*

Oak or lindenwood, H. 10 inches (25.4 cm.), W. 5-3/8 inches (13.2 cm.), D. 2-3/4 inches (7.0 cm.)

A North Netherlandish counterpart to the Brabantine "St. George Baptizing the Pagan King" (no. 67), this Madonna and Child in wood probably formed part of a high-relief narrative scene from the early life of Christ, one of a set of reliefs for an altarpiece. Iconographic evidence speaks in favor of the Adoration of Magi as the scene originally represented. The woodcarver, a contemporary of the great Adriaen van Wessel, reveals in his work an aesthetic preference for the simple and unadorned. His choice of Madonna type is rooted in a familiarity with and respect for the rural peasant life of the North, which he lends noble interpretation. It is this and the economy of means employed in executing the design that make up this artist's formula for intimacy and charm.

EX COLLECTION: [Edward R. Lubin, New York].

PLATE LIX

Lent by William College Museum of Art,
Williamstown, Massachusetts

69 FRANCO-FLEMISH, late 15th century

*St. James the Elder as a Pilgrim*

Limestone, H. 39 inches (99.1 cm.)

For want of a better term to describe works of art in the Flemish style of around 1500 which could have been produced either in the north of France or in the Netherlands, the term "Franco-Flemish" still is often applied to sculptures such as this standing St. James the Elder. Perhaps the possibility that the figure is by a Flemish artist working in Spain—in which case it would be "Hispano-Flemish" —should not be ruled out, though in the light of present knowledge an origin in the northernmost part of France, in Picardy or the Artois, seems likely. The super-abundant details of wrinkled skin and seemingly wet locks of hair, buttons and leather straps for the costume, rope sandals and the ornaments on the hat, gear consisting of pilgrim's staff, bottle, and rosary, and pages of the opened book, recorded *ad infinitum,* are characteristic of the style. Much undercutting is employed in achieving realistic effects; particularly notable are the gaps in the buttoned opening of the long garment which expose part of the chest.

St. James was venerated throughout France and Spain during the Later Middle Ages, but he was also very popular in Flanders. An interesting and little-known altarpiece in the form of a triptych, painted by an anonymous late fifteenth-century Flemish artist and now preserved in the John Herron Institute of Arts in Indianapolis, Indiana, depicts an extensive cycle of scenes from the pilgrim saint's life and is decorated on the exterior with the same ornaments worn here on his hat.

REFERENCES: University of Kansas Museum of Art *Handbook*, Lawrence, 1962, p. 32; Marilyn Stokstad, *The Medieval Collections of the Museum of Art,* University of Kansas, Lawrence, 1963, no. 22, p. 12, ill. p. 12.

PLATE LXIII

The University of Kansas Museum of Art, 56.34

70 FRANCO-FLEMISH, late 15th or early 16th century

*Fragment of a Relief of the Crucifixion*

Alabaster with traces of polychromy and gilt, H. 19-1/2 inches (49.5 cm.), W. 24 inches (61.9 cm.)

In viewing this fragmentary relief of the "Crucifixion," one should, perhaps, readily recall the voussoir figures of ca. 1425 for the west portal of Saint-Antoine-en-Viennois (Isère). The heavily molded forms, the thick drapery that spills out over the knees, the hunched-over figures almost swallowed by tucks and folds of garments—all the traits of Burgundian-influenced sculpture of roughly seventy-five years before—seem to be donned for a Sluter centennary. Could it be that there was a conscious revival of Claus Sluter in sculpture as there was of Jan van Eyck in painting of around 1500? If so, the leader probably would have been another Netherlander, and our fragment from a "Crucifixion" would qualify for consideration as one of the truest expressions of the movement. One has only to compare such a work with contemporary sculptures of northern France in the *détente* style (see nos. 58-60) to appreciate the quality of realism expressed in this work. The Italianate motifs on the bearded soldier's leg-armor provide the evidence for dating the piece at the beginning of the Renaissance in the North.

The traces of polychromy and gilding show that originally this work was very rich in surface effects.

EX COLLECTION: Frank Gair Macomber, Boston.

EXHIBITIONS: Lille, France, Musée des Beaux-Arts, n.d.

REFERENCES: William H. Forsyth, in Metropolitan Museum of Art *Bulletin*, XXXII, 1937, p. 68, ill.; Sale catalogue of the Frank Gair Macomber Collection at the American Art Association, no. 553.

PLATE LXII

Lent by The Metropolitan Museum of Art,
New York, Rogers Fund, 36.146.1

71 FRANCO-FLEMISH, early 16th century

*A Falconer (Philippe le beau ?)*

Polychromed limestone, H. 43-3/4 inches (1.11 m.)

The identification of the falconer as Philippe le Beau rests on the somewhat inconclusive evidence that a lion—interpreted as the lion of Burgundy—rests at his feet. Philippe, or Philip the Handsome (not to be confused with Philippe le Bel, or Philip the Fair, of around 1300), was the son of Mary of Burgundy and Maximilian of Austria. Through Mary of Burgundy's marriage to the son of a Habsburg emperor in 1477 the Habsburgs had gained control over Burgundy and the Netherlands and were to maintain their dominance in the Netherlands until nearly the end of the eighteenth century. Philip, their son, was wed to the princess of Castile, known as Joan the Mad, the daughter of the King of Spain, in 1496; thereby the Habsburg connections in Spain were secured. Sometime after Philip the Handsome's death (1506), his son by Joan the Mad, Charles (b. 1500 in Ghent), could be put on the Spanish throne as Charles V.

It is difficult to say whether this stone sculpture actually represents Philip. He does not wear the Order of the Golden Fleece which was his and his father's to wear. The face bears little resemblance to any of his authenticated painted portraits—most of them, admittedly, youthful—nor to the sculpted bust (formerly full-figure) now in the John Herron Institute of Arts in Indianapolis, Indiana. A conjunction of two factors, or rather three, makes the identification plausible:

the sculpture is Franco-Flemish in style (not Burgundian), Philip was made Regent of the Netherlands by Maximilian and resided there, and Philip was very popular.

REFERENCES: Otto Karl Bach, in Denver Art Museum *Quarterly,* Winter, 1955, p. 40, no. 101, ill.

PLATE LXXII

Lent by The Denver Art Museum,
Charles Bayly Collection, E-634

72  FRANCE (Champagne [Troyes?]), early 16th century

*Virgin and Child with Two Angels*

Limestone, H. 20-3/4 inches (52.7 cm.) with base, W. 12-3/8 inches (31.4 cm.)

With the death of Charles the Bold, Duke of Burgundy, in the Battle of Nancy in 1477, the political and cultural hegemony of Burgundy came to an end. Paris was no longer a metropolis of art, and the French court was wherever the King chose to reside, usually in the provinces. The revival of courtly art was not to be seen until the reign of Louis XII, the "second Caesar," and Anne of Brittany (1499-1515). Louis XI was a bourgeois king, and Charles VIII led a vogue for Italian art during his reign. During Charles VIII's time Champagne became the most prosperous region of France, and it continued to produce works of art for the local, wealthy middle-class patrons well into the sixteenth century. The "Virgin and Child with Two Angels" exhibited here is a characteristic example from the sculpture workshops active in Champagne, especially in its most important city, Troyes (cf. Raymond Koechlin and J. J. Marquet de Vasselot, *La Sculpture à Troyes et dans la Champagne,* Paris, 1900; *L'Art en Champagne au Moyen-âge* [exhibition catalogue], Paris, Musée de l'Orangerie, 1959). The group with the Virgin *lactens* has humble, middle-class appeal and emphasizes typically the large, heavy hands and heavy cheeks. The long hair flowing down the shoulders and back and the drapery broken up into many folds are characteristic of the region. It is interesting to compare this group with the figures represented on the chiseled iron tabernacle door of certain Troyes provenance, also shown here (no. 120). The head of the left angel in our sculpture and that of St. John on the tabernacle door are virtually the same, and the indented places in the folds of this Virgin's drapery are similarly found in the drapery of the Virgin on the tabernacle door. The stone sculpture is executed in a very soft stone of the Champagne region that makes the piece very fragile.

REFERENCES: *Cloisters Guide,* New York, 1926, p. 34; Joseph Breck in Metropolitan Museum of Art *Bulletin,* XXI, 1926, p. 118.

PLATE LXIII

Lent by The Metropolitan Museum of Art,
Cloisters Collection, New York, 26.63.37

73  FRANCE, late 15th century

*St. Louis of Toulouse: panel*

Oak, H. 28-7/8 inches (73.3 cm.), W. 9-1/2 inches (24.1 cm.)

This is an unusual representation of St. Louis of Toulouse, for he wears the ermine-trimmed royal robes that would have been his with the throne of Naples had he not refused them for a life in the Order of St. Francis. But the arms with the bishop's staff signifying his office as Bishop of Toulouse (until his death in 1297), clearly indicate that this is Louis (not to be confused with Louis IX, King of France, who was his great uncle). He is shown here with the fleur-de-lis embroidered on his garments and standing on a console beneath a Late Gothic arch with foliate decoration. The panel may have decorated a choirstall or some other piece of ecclesiastical furniture. Similar carved panels, dated early sixteenth century, were formerly in the Marquise de Arconati-Visconti Collection (cf. Émile Molinier, *Les Meubles du Moyen-âge et de la Renaissance,* Paris, n.d., ill. p. 11).

Lent by The Walters Art Gallery,
Baltimore, 64.14

PLATE LXIV

74 FRANCE, early 16th century

*A Donor with St. John the Evangelist*

Polychromed oak, H. 12-7/8 inches (32.8 cm.)

Lent by The Walters Art Gallery,
Baltimore, 61.86

75 FRANCE (?), 15th century

*Flamboyant Gothic arch and rosette design: panel*

Oak, H. 44-1/2 inches (1.129 m.), W. 20-3/8 inches (0.517 m.)

This carved wood panel of Late Gothic architectural design is from a piece of furniture, but the design could just as easily have been translated into stone— for example, for the decoration of the end wall of a cathedral transept. Viewed in this way, the "wall" tends to dissolve because of the super-abundance of tracery and ornament. The principal motif is the ogee arch with its organically con- ceived foliate decoration, under which are developed geometric patterns based on the circle and other curvilinear forms that are divided and subdivided. This example may, in fact, be English, but there is so much exchange between England and France at the time that it is impossible to say definitely. The motifs in the third tier of tracery suggest a fan-vault translated into two-dimension.

Lent by The Seattle Art Museum,
Purchase from the Bequest
of Edith Decatur, 54.Go.13.1

PLATE LXVI

76 FRANCE, late 15th century

*Interlacing arch and rosette design: panel from a choirstall*

Oak, H. 36-1/2 inches (92.7 cm.), W. 19-3/4 inches (50.1 cm.)

Like another carved wooden panel included in this exhibition (no. 75), this was made for the decoration of furniture. The panel is known to have come from the church at Bourg-en-Bresse (Ain) in France. Conceptually and technically it is a masterpiece in the design and carving of woodwork. Here, more than in the other example exhibited, the flamboyant Gothic design defies the laws of engi- neering and is enjoyed completely for the possibilities of ornamental effect. The tracery forms a screen in which the integral parts seem to produce continual movement and have the ability to change.

PROVENANCE: Bourg-en-Bresse (Ain), Church.

## SMALL CARVINGS IN IVORY, BONE, AND BOXWOOD

77   PARIS, ca. 1335-1350

*Scenes of the Early Life and Passion of Christ: leaf of a diptych*

Ivory, H. 5-15/16 inches (15.1 cm.), W. 4 inches (10.1 cm.)

The hinge marks on the left edge of this ivory plaque show that it was originally the right half of a diptych. It is typical of the production of early fourteenth-century Parisian ateliers whose specialty was large diptychs of the Passion. The present diptych leaf is related by the exhuberance of its style to the second and later of the two great Parisian ateliers of the first half of the century and, as is commonly the case, relates scenes of the early life of Christ in the lower part with ones from His Passion in the upper part. Represented are the Adoration of the Magi, the Presentation in the Temple, the Crucifixion, and the Resurrection. The use of models in the workshop explains the close similarity of compositions in numerous diptychs and diptych leaves, even when the combination of scenes is not the same. The arcades of crocheted arches and gables with organic leaf decoration characteristically organize the scenes into horizontal registers as well as provide the unifying decoration. This particular leaf combines in one-half of a diptych scenes which are often spread out over the two halves. The space is therefore somewhat crowded.

The Adoration of the Magi in our diptych leaf is closely paralleled in style and composition by the same scene in a diptych formerly in the Schoolmeesters Collection in Liège, whose provenance is the convent of the Welsh Nuns in Trier (cf. Raymond Koechlin, *Les Ivoires gothiques français*, Paris, 1924, II, no. 783). In the Liège diptych the scenes also begin at the bottom, and the Crucifixion appears above the scene of the Nativity in the left wing. The same scenes displayed in the left half of the Liège diptych form the subject matter of a small diptych in the Metropolitan Museum in New York (cf. M. B. Freeman, in Metropolitan Museum *Bulletin,* XI, 1952, pp. 108-115), in which the Crucifixion in the right wing nearly duplicates the Crucifixion in our leaf. Although there is one more figure in each of the groups to the side of the cross in the Metropolitan diptych, the Virgin's drapery is identically rendered, and the motif of the female figure behind the swooning Virgin supporting her with both hands held around her waist is repeated. Though dryer in execution, the Metropolitan diptych also displays the *fleuronné* gables that appear on our diptych leaf. The relationship of the Parisian ateliers of ivory carvers to those of the manuscript illuminators has not been adequately studied; however, the influence of Jean Pucelle's lively style in illustrating with figures is felt in the works of ivory carvers dating from shortly before 1350. Illustrations in manuscripts from his workshop, for example, the *Hours of Yolande de Flandre* (London, British Museum, Yates Thompson ms. no. 27), can be compared with the scenes on this diptych leaf.

*The Siege of the Castle of Love: mirror back*

Ivory, H. 4-1/2, W. 4-1/4 inches

The courtly style of the Parisian ateliers of the early fourteenth century is be-stowed with especially lavish results upon small objects of ivory for secular use, such as mirror backs. In the stylistic sub-category of mirror backs to which this superb example belongs—that is, those which have a circle-within-a-square design with grotesque animals in the four corners—elegance and decorativeness combine with stereotyped convention and a sense of naïvité in depicting a scene of courtly romance. The subject is the hero's futile siege against and eventual surrender to the stronghold of love, and the literary source is that most popular secular work of the Later Middle Ages, the *Roman de la Rose*. Written from about 1240 by Guillaume de Loris and completed before 1280 by Jean de Meung, the famous poetic work commemorates the forms of aristocratic love more sublimely than any other Late Medieval text. The love symbol is the rose, here depicted as the maiden's sole weapon of defense. But in the mirror back the roses in the hands of maidens are no less stylized and purely decorative than those used to ornament a hero's shield and a horse's festive dress to the right, a perfect example of the merging of artistic convention and the conventions of an elite society. The same sentiments of surrender to love are carried forth a century later than our ivory in René d'Anjou's literary work, *Livre du cuer d'amours espris*. But King René's love melodrama unfolds less through a complex system of metaphors than it does through actors who are themselves allegorical figures. His symbol of love is the heart itself, and his luxury manuscript of the text, now in the National-bibliothek in Vienna, is illustrated with miniatures in a style of uncompromising realism.

In our ivory mirror back, mounted knights in armor assail the Castle of Love in mock fashion, while already at the sides heroes are surrendering to the power of love, having discovered the key that can unlock the castle: courteous request. The knight at the extreme left, dismounted and without shield, offers his sword to the lady above, handing it to her hilt-first. The stylized trees, the rough, rocky terrain along the bottom foreground, and even the organically conceived finials on the castle towers, indicate an awakening sense of naturalism that can be docu-mented in Parisian ateliers as early as 1296 with the *Breviary of Philippe le Bel*. The lively scene of the siege is a world unto itself, paraded around at a lazy pace by four sleepy and amiable dragons or wyverns.

An ivory mirror back of less fine execution than this, but of similar style and with dragons in the four corners, was sold recently at Sotheby's (April 17, 1969). Another in the Victoria and Albert Museum in London (Inv. no. 9-72), of later date than the present example and with lions as rim decorations, represents the same theme as ours but includes Amor at the top of the castle drawing his bow at the women. Robert Calkins cites yet another and even closer representation on a mirror back formerly in the Sulzbach Collection in Paris and mentions that the London example has recently been relocalized to Cologne.

EX COLLECTION: Baroness Lambert, Brussels; Baron Gustave de Rothschild, Paris.

EXHIBITIONS: Cleveland Museum of Art, "Treasures from Medieval France," 1966-1967, no. V-19; Ithaca, New York, Cornell University, Andrew Dickson White Museum of Art, "A Medieval Treasury," 1968, no. 81.

REFERENCES: Sherman E. Lee, in *Art Quarterly*, XII, Spring, 1949, pp. 191 ff., ill. p. 188; Seattle Art Museum *Handbook*, 1951, p. 116; William Wixom, *Treasures from Medieval France* (exhibition catalogue), 1967, p. 206, no. V-19, ill. p. 207; Robert G. Calkins, *A Medieval Treasury* (exhibition catalogue), Ithaca, 1968, no. 81, pp. 9, 157-158, ill. p. (77).

PLATE IV

Lent by The Seattle Art Museum,<br>Donald E. Frederick Memorial Collection.  Fr.10.1

79   FRANCE, third quarter of the 14th century

*A Hunting Party: mirror back*

Ivory, H. 3-5/8 inches  (9.3 cm.), W. 3-3/4 inches  (9.6 cm.)

A courting couple taking part in the hunt with falcons is depicted on this mirror back.  At the left, also on horseback, is a third member of the party blowing a hunting horn.  The scene is enclosed by a circular frame with a decorative interior design of seven half-circles.  Grotesque masks appear in the spandrel-shaped interspaces.  The riding group repeats all but one figure of the composition in the famous ivory mirror back formerly in the Spitzer Collection and now in the Metropolitan Museum in New York (cf. Stella Rubinstein-Bloch, *The George and Florence Blumenthal Collection,* New York, 1926; see also Donald D. Egbert, in *Art Studies,* VII, 1929, pp. 169-206).  Besides omitting a second female figure, a hat worn by the first male figure, and a running dog in the foreground, our ivory has a flatter appearance than the Spitzer ivory and shows less of the profuse foliage in the background.  The scene in the Spitzer ivory is enclosed by an octafoil instead of a septafoil design, and in the corners of the outside margin appear prancing lions instead of triangular leaf forms.  The direction in which the lions are turned in the Spitzer ivory determines that it must have been the second valve of a mirror case, the first valve of which may have appeared somewhat like the one representing the "Siege of the Castle of Love" in the Victoria and Albert Museum in London (see no. 78).

EX COLLECTION:  Octave Homberg, Paris; J. Pierpont Morgan, New York.

REFERENCES:  Raymond Koechlin, *Les Ivoires gothiques français,* Paris, 1924, II, no. 1030.

PLATE V

Lent by The Metropolitan Museum of Art, New York,<br>Gift of J. Pierpont Morgan, 17.190.248

80   FRANCE, 14th century

*Toilet accessory used in parting the hair*

Ivory, H. 11-3/4 inches  (30.0 cm.)

This is a toilet accessory known as a *gravoire* in French, used for parting a woman's hair (for texts concerning the use of the *gravoire,* see Victor Gay, *Glossaire archéologique,* 1887, I, p. 794).  The subject represented is one of courtly love and may be derived from one of the chivalrous romances like *Tristram and Iseult.*  Similar objects are known that are thought to be French (cf. Raymond Koechlin, *Les Ivoires gothiques français,* Paris, 1924, I, pp. 416-419, II, nos. 1122-1138, II, pls. CLXXXIX, CIXC; sale catalogue of the Émile Lévy Collection at the Hôtel Drouot, Paris, Dec. 14, 1928, p. 8, no. 11, ill.).  Others are called Italian (cf. *Berlin-Museen. Drei Jahre national-sozialistischer Museumsarbeit. Erwerbungen 1933-1935* (exhibition catalogue), Berlin, Schlossmuseum, 1936, pp. 204-205, nos. 181, 182).

EX COLLECTION:  J. Pierpont Morgan, New York.

Lent by The Metropolitan Museum of Art, New York,
Anonymous Gift in memory of
the late J. Pierpont Morgan, 18.71

PLATE IV

81 PARIS, 14th century

*La Chastelaine de Vergi: panel from a casket*

Ivory, H. 3-9/16 inches (9.0 cm.), W. 9-7/16 inches (24.0 cm.)

EX COLLECTION: Engel-Gros, Ripaille, France; M. Boy, Paris.; [Edward R. Lubin, New York].

REFERENCES: Sale catalogue of the M. Boy Collection, Galerie Georges Petit, Paris, May 15 and 25, 1905, p. 56, no. 279; *Collection Engel-Gros* (sale catalogue), Galerie Georges Petit, Paris, May 30-31, June 1, 1921, p. 75, no. 143; Raymond Koechlin, *Les Ivoires gothiques français,* Paris, 1924, II, p. 509 n. (as Engel-Gros, no. 1305), p. 513; Michael Locey, in University of Kansas Museum of Art *Register,* III, Fall, 1970.

The University of Kansas Museum of Art,
Gift of Friends of the Museum, 66.5

PLATE V

82 FRANCE, second half of the fourteenth century

*Jousting Scene: panel from a casket*

Ivory, H. 2-3/4 inches (7.0 cm.), W. 7-1/2 inches (19.1 cm.)

The panoramic treatment of this ivory plaque sets it apart from the usual fourteenth-century French plaques made for the sides of small caskets. Instead of being broken into separate scenes or segments of a scene by raised vertical strips that provide a place for attaching bands of silver, this plaque displays the jousting scene in continuous, uninterrupted fashion, like the carved long-panels on late fourteenth-century wooden chests. A similar scene is represented on what was once the lid of a casket, formerly in the Oppenheim Collection and now in the Metropolitan Museum of Art (cf. Robert G. Calkins, *A Medieval Treasury* [exhibition catalogue], Ithaca, 1968, p. 157, no. 80, ill.). Absent are the amorous couples that more poignantly and significantly relate the theme of proof of knightly courage and honor on the jousting grounds to the ritual of courtly love. Added, however, is the interest of players of musical instruments other than trumpets—a bagpiper and a percussionist. Above, in the center, a royal couple and members of their court review the proceedings below, while at the left a princess receives advice and gestures her opinion.

EX COLLECTION: J. Pierpont Morgan, New York.

Lent by The Metropolitan Museum of Art, New York,
Gift of J. Pierpont Morgan, 17.190.249

PLATE IV

83 NORTHERN FRANCE, late 14th century

*Standing Virgin and Child*

Ivory, H. 6-9/16 inches (16.7 cm.)

Together with diptychs and small shrines carved of ivory, small figures of the Virgin for devotional purposes figure prominently among the objects produced in the ivory carvers' workshops in France during the fourteenth century. However, this is a most unusual ivory statuette, for in style and conception it is unlike the idealized type of Madonna usually produced in the Ile-de-France. It has a stronger emotional appeal stemming from the expressive faces of the Virgin and Child and from the treatment of the hair and drapery. It is therefore ascribed to northern France rather than to the area of which Paris is the center. The weight of the upper body and particularly of the heavy shoulders is keenly felt by the artist. One has the feeling that the Virgin could walk away from the cascading folds of drapery which are a convention of the time, because her garments are otherwise wrapped tightly around her body. There is a marked sense of observation displayed by features such as the hands and the fingernails, and no less evident is the realistic interpretation of the Christ Child's playful attitude. The new, intimate relationship between the Madonna and the Child in works of art had been initiated only about the middle of the fourteenth century under the influence of German art. In short, this is far from the aristocratic Madonnas known in French art before 1400. It is not difficult to believe that the statuette might have been created by or in association with the numerous artists of lower Rhenish and eastern Netherlandish origin who were employed in France around 1400. In this case, one would have to place the work in the courtly circles of Philip the Bold of Burgundy, Jean de Berry, and Charles VI of France.

EX COLLECTION: Mayer-Fuld.

REFERENCES: Catalogue of the Mayer-Fuld Collection, no. 145; *The Buckingham Medieval Collection,* Art Institute of Chicago, 1945, p. 70, no. 49, pl. XXII.

PLATE VIII

Lent by The Art Institute of Chicago,
Buckingham Fund, 43.62

84  FRANCE, early 15th century

*The Gift of the Rose: mirror back*

Ivory, H. 4-1/8 inches (10.5 cm.), W. 4 inches (10.2 cm.)

This carved mirror back is related in style to a group of ivories believed to have been produced in North Italy because of their similarity to the ivories made in the workshop of the Embriachi family in Venice (cf. [Philippe Verdier], in *The International Style* [exhibition catalogue], Baltimore, 1962, p. 119, no. 121, pl. CII). This group, dating mostly from the first quarter of the fifteenth century, is characterized by the sharp outlines and stiff attitudes of the figures, in contrast to the Ile-de-France models on which they are based. A second group with a characteristic vine-scroll border motif that also resembles the characteristic decoration of an Embriachi ivory, and perhaps dating from the second and third quarters of the century, is also disputed as to origin between France and Italy (see nos. 85, 86). However, the first group—to which the present ivory belongs—is early enough and shows enough dissimilarities with the Embriachi ivories to warrant the supposition that works belonging to this group were produced in a provincial workshop in southern or southeastern France bordering on Switzerland, and that it was to some extent on these models rather than ones from the Ile-de-France that the Embriachi ivories were based. In turn, ivories from Venice were imported into France on such a large scale that they could have influenced the second group of French ivories produced in the second and third quarters of the century.

The example here shows a pair of lovers between a tree and a castle framed in a six-lobed medallion which is ornamented in the spandels with masks. The framing arrangement is nearly the same as in the Ile-de-France mirror case of about a century earlier here on exhibition (no. 79). The theme is reminiscent of the "Siege of the Castle of Love" (no. 78); the woman proceeding from her castle of defense is offering the rose to the gentleman, who, unlike the knights in the earlier ivory, is defenseless from the outset.

EX COLLECTION: Bourgeois Frères.

REFERENCES: Sale catalogue of the Bourgeois Frères Collection, Cologne, October 19-27, 1904, no. 1082, ill.

PLATE V

Lent by The Walters Art Gallery, Baltimore, 71.281

85  FRANCE, 15th century

*Jousting Scene and Bathing Scene: lady's comb*

Ivory, H. 4-7/8 inches (12.4 cm.), W. 5-3/4 inches (14.1 cm.)

A yet unfully interpreted pair of scenes of courtly romance decorates the two sides of this perfectly preserved ivory comb. On one side, a jousting scene between two knights mounted on horseback is elevated above the world of reality by the stylization of their flying cloaks which makes them appear as wings—a most unusual motif. The other side represents in two parts a bathing scene and a scene in a bed chamber, both of which are far more down-to-earth. Robert Calkins has interpreted the two sides as representing the ritual preparation of a knight before he goes into the lists, including the ceremony of a bath in a tub from which sprouts a rose—this is supposedly a reminder of his chivalric goal in love—followed by his constant vigil until daylight and the beginning of the tournament. But unless we are to suppose that medieval knights wore women's headgear in private, and in spite of the ambiguous anatomy displayed in the domestic scenes, we must conclude that all three figures on that side of the comb are women. The rose is the lady's until she presents it to her hero; knights have beds with only one pillow. In short, this is the woman's world of reality in which hope has sprung; it is complemented on the other side by a representation of her world of fantasy. Since the one side is in narrative style and the other one displays a symbolic, heraldic character, the symbolic relation of one side to the other is explained also in terms of style. The knight does not actually enter into the picture at all, for in this comb for a lady's use the lady's point of view reigns. In fact, it has already been noticed by Stanley Ferber that "the lances, armor, and the horses alleviate the possibility of real battle, but rather seem to indicate a mock or symbolic battle of honor."

Ferber has also pointed out that the vine-scroll and rope-twist borders on this comb are well conceived and well executed. Let us say that were they better conceived and executed they would detract from the unified expression in the figures and ornament. The characteristic rope pattern is also found on North Italian ivories of similar or slightly earlier date, specifically one whose style Calkins sees reflected in the present example (cf. [Philippe Verdier], in *The International Style* [exhibition catalogue], Baltimore, 1962, p. 120, no. 122, pl. CII). This is an argument not to be lost in suggesting that there is a mutual exchange between ivory carvers of France and North Italy during the first half of the fifteenth century (see no. 84).

EXHIBITIONS: Binghamton, New York, State University of New York, University Art Gallery, "Developments in the Early Renaissance," 1968, no. 21; Ithaca, New York, Cornell University, Andrew Dickson White Museum of Art, "A Medieval Treasury," 1968, no. 84.

REFERENCES: S[tanley] F[erber], in *Developments in the Early Renaissance* (exhibition catalogue), Binghamton, 1968, p. 27, no. 21, ill.; Robert G. Calkins, *A Medieval Treasury* (exhibition catalogue), Ithaca, 1968, p. 159, no. 84, ill.

PLATE XVIII

Lent by the Paul Drey Gallery, New York

**86 FRANCE, third quarter (?) of the 15th century**

*Casket*

Polychromed and gilded bone and ivory, H. 3-13/16 inches (9.7 cm.), W. 5-1/2 inches (14.0 cm.), D. 6-3/8 inches (16.2 cm.)

This entire, well preserved casket of bone is in a style and technique that place it with a number of other known ivory and bone carvings of undetermined origin. This group invites much conjecture as to dating and localization, but there is no solid evidence. The group certainly shows the influence of North Italian ivories, especially ones of the Embriachi (see no. 84), but are themselves probably not Italian. One might suggest that they were produced in ateliers located somewhere in southern or southeastern France—in the Lyonnais, Dauphiné, Savoie, even Provence. The fact that individually they are usually dated by style anywhere between 1400 and the late fifteenth century leads one to believe that many are dated either too early or too late. It would seem that the mean production falls in the middle decades of the fifteenth century. Some of the costumes of figures on this casket are represented in the *Livre des Tournois du Roi René* of ca. 1460-1465 (Paris, Bibliothèque de l'Arsenal), but they were probably worn somewhat earlier.

On the top and back panels of the casket are represented pairs of lovers playing musical instruments; between each pair stands a tree or fountain. Stylized suns shine happily on the couples, and plants spring out of the ground. The long sides are devoted to indoor and out-of-door merriment—the ribaldry of a female dancer with two male acrobat partners and a jester performing to the rhythm and drones of a musician doubling as piper and percussionist; the spirited chase of the stag, which is driven by leaping dogs right into the marksman's range of arrow-shot. On the front, wild men holding clubs guard the lock. The ritual of chivalry that typifies scenes of romance on fourteenth-century ivories (see nos. 78, 81, 82) is markedly absent. The polychromy and gilding add much surface luster to the object; the bottom is a checkerboard pattern of bone and tortoiseshell. The brass lock and the hinges are of later date.

PLATE XIX

Lent by The Art Museum, Princeton University, Princeton, New Jersey, 59-11

**87 FRANCE, second half of the 15th century**

*Scenes with Lovers: panel from a casket*

Ivory, H. 2-1/4 inches (5.7 cm.), W. 9 inches (22.9 cm.)

Scenes of lovers exchanging gifts are represented on this long, carved panel from an ivory casket. Flowers, a pearl (?), and even an ape (symbolizing sensuality) are given and received. The four scenes are similar to those representd on the carved bone casket also exhibited here (no. 86), and this ivory is also technically related to the other work. The backgrounds of both are cross-hatched with incised lines, and above the elaborate arches of the ivory panel are to be seen the *rinceaux* also found on the bone casket. The figures on the ivory panel move with a grace and freedom typically French, and their costumes and short proportions relate them directly to the ivory comb included among the secular objects in this exhibition (no. 85). The nodding ogee arch resting on two columns attached at the sides to the "piers" (devices used to separate the scenes and to provide a place for attaching the silver clasps that are now missing), forms the recurrent decorative motif throughout the four scenes of the panel. In subject matter and costume the scenes are reminiscent of some of the earliest printed engravings preserved from the 1430's (for example, the famous large "Garden of Love").

EX COLLECTION: Henry Walters, Baltimore, 1925.

Lent by The Walters Art Gallery,
Baltimore, 71.204

PLATE XVIII

88   FRANCE, third quarter of the 15th century

*Falcon Hood Stand with later* (?) *Falcon Hood*

Ivory, H. 4 inches (10.2 cm.), W. 2-1/4 inches (5.7 cm.), D. 2-1/4 inches (5.7 cm.)

This is an exceedingly rare object of secular use, its undecorated bulbous top providing a place for a hood used in falconry to rest like a wig on a wig stand. At the higher end of the carved base beneath the relief crown is a niche presumably designed to hold a *champlevé* enamel coat-of-arms. Koechlin knew of only one other example of this type, the one formerly in the Figdor Collection in Vienna (*Ivoires*, II, no. 1251, p. 437, pl. CCV) bearing the inscription: *nunc aut quondam.* Beigbeder cites another example in Florence as German and mentions that such stands were also made in Italy.

The design and carving of this piece, with its roughly outlined border *rinceaux* and cross-hatched relief background, reminds one of a number of coffrets and other objects made either of bone or ivory that are usually assigned a French origin, although their exact provenance is not known. The dating here is based upon a comparison of the carving with that on the bone coffret of similar style included in this exhibition (no. 86), but in fact it may date as early as the middle of the fifteenth century. The *fleur-de-lis* in the crown and the running pattern of *fleur-de-lis* in the relief are an indication that its origin is French, although this evidence is by no means conclusive. The simple design and the unassuming style of execution should not be deemed to reflect upon the position and wealth of the original owner. Falconry was the sport of kings and nobles, and the crown-bearing archway on the face of this object is imbued with the symbolism of royalty.

EX COLLECTION: Georges Chalandon, Paris; [Adolph Loewi, Los Angeles].

EXHIBITIONS: Lyon, 1877, no. 808; Paris, "Exposition du Moyen-âge" 1913, no. 124, as "une Poignée massive" or a seal.

REFERENCES: (exhibition catalogue), Lyon, 1877, no. 808; *Exposition du Moyen-âge* (exhibition catalogue), Paris, 1913, no. 124; Raymond Koechlin, *Les Ivoires gothiques français*, Paris, 1924, II, p. 437, no. 1250; O. Beigbeder, *Ivory*, New York, 1965, p. 77, fig. 71.

Lent by The Detroit Institute of Arts,
Hill Memorial Fund, 66.128 (stand), 66.127 (hood)

PLATE LXXII

89   NETHERLANDS, ca. 1500

*The Lamentation over Christ*

Ivory, H. 6 inches (15.3 cm.), W. 5 inches (12.7 cm.), D. 2 inches (5.0 cm.)

Carvings in ivory, especially figured compositions like this one, are exceptional for the North during the late fifteenth century and early sixteenth. It is an interesting thought that the piece originally may have belonged to an entire series representing the Passion. In style and composition it is analogous to a number of small Netherlandish and lower Rhenish wood sculptures (cf. especially the "Lamentation" in the Bode-Museum in East Berlin, ill. *Spätgotische niederländische Bildwerke,* Skulpturen-Sammlung, Staatliche Museen zu Berlin, 1962, no. 15, fig. 18).

PLATE LXII                                                            Lent anonymously

90   FRANCE or FLANDERS, early 16th century

*Memento mori: rosary bead*

Ivory, H. 2 inches  (5.0 cm.)

A recurrent theme in fifteenth-century art, and one which appears with increasing frequency as the sixteenth century is approached, is that of death in the form of a skeleton or skull. This *memento mori* combines the icon representation of the head of Christ—the image on the veil of St. Veronica—with the skull and the head of a woman (usually interpreted as the Virgin). The three are joined together back-to-back in an irregularly rounded shape pierced vertically for suspension. Most probably it was used as the primary bead on a rosary.

Lent by The Walters Art Gallery,
Baltimore, 71.326

91   FLANDERS, ca. 1500

*The Crucifixion and Resurrection: rosary bead*

Boxwood, Diam. 2 inches  (5.0 cm.)

Among the most remarkable objects of Netherlandish craftsmanship from the Late Gothic period are certain pieces easily overlooked because of their minute size. This rosary bead, for example, incorporates two intricately-carved scenes from the Passion of Christ with figures barely visible to the naked eye. The Netherlandish tendency to depict the visible world seen distantly with the same accuracy as that seen at close range is matched by the tendency to reduce what is readily observable to a miniature scale. The rosary bead causes one to think back to Jan van Eyck and to Panofsky's statement that Van Eyck's eye "operates as a microscope and as a telescope at the same time—and it is amusing to think that both these instruments were to be invented . . ." in the Netherlands . . ." (*Early Netherlandish Painting,* Cambridge, Mass., 1953, p. 182).

Lent by The Walters Art Gallery,
PLATE LVIII                                                          Baltimore, 61.132

# GOLDSMITH'S WORK, ENAMELS, METALWORK AND LEATHER

92   WEST SWITZERLAND-BURGUNDY, ca. 1360

*The Montferrand Casket*

Incised, punched and embossed leather with parcel-gilt red copper mountings, H. 5-3/8 inches (13.5 cm.), W. 16-3/8 inches (41.0 cm.), D. 5-1/4 inches (13.0 cm.)

This small, narrow chest or casket has several unusual features which, taken together, identify it as belonging to a category extremely rare among known surviving examples of European leather caskets of the Later Middle Ages. It can be designated by the German generic term *Minnekästchen* or "minne-casket," a term which grew out of the modern romantic period to refer to the type of small chest or casket containing precious gifts from a knight to the lady whose favor he sought (see Günter Gall, *Leder im europäischen Kunsthandwerk*, Braunschweig, 1965). That it has a long narrow shape, a flattened hip-roof, and both the characteristic subject matter for decorating a minne-casket and at opposite ends the coats-of-arms of two family houses (indicating its use as a marriage casket) is indicative of its uniqueness and importance. The casket was formerly assigned to Italy. Gall has recently published a survey of the armorial bearings which shows that the arms are those of the Montferrand (canton of Vaud, Switzerland) and Savoy families. On the basis of these, the stylistic evidence of other caskets in Turin and Offenbach-am-Main, and the evidence of flat incising and light punching characteristic of the workshop of the so-called "Master with the Boar" in the region of Switzerland, Gall has concluded that the casket is the product of a previously unknown workshop located in the region of West Switzerland and Burgundy. Following the evidence for a dating of the casket in Offenbach-am-Main to the year 1363, and using comparisons for items of costume worn by the figures with other securely dated works, Gall has arrived at a date of ca. 1360 for our casket. Therefore, the Montferrand Casket would seem to carry on the techniques used in the Master with the Boar leather workshop, which was active around 1330, possibly in the canton of Graubünden.

The subject matter of our casket, described in detail by Gall, consists primarily of busts of knights and ladies and figures of animals of fable, and birds, all encircled by floral wreaths. Across the front of the casket, the busts of knights and ladies are arranged in fours, alternating with similarly grouped decorations representing grotesque animals. In the center of each of the longer extreme left and right sections is inserted the standing figure of a nobleman and of a lady, respectively. Further busts alternating with ornamental leaf decorations form the incised patterns on the back; drolleries of mixed human and animal forms, birds, busts, and foliage decorate the long sides of the cover; and two men, one wearing a crown and the other wearing a brimmed hat, adorn the two ends beneath the coat-of-arms. Remains of colored paint show that the casket was originally polychromed in order to give the original motifs more separation from the background and from one another. Parcel-gilded metal fittings, including the lock, handle, corner fittings, and straps decorated with rosettes, complete the rich surface embellishment.

CONDITION: Part of the center strap of metal on the lid missing, the edge fitting for the right lid end also missing.

EX COLLECTION: Foulc, Paris.

EXHIBITIONS: Boston, Museum of Fine Arts, "Arts of the Middle Ages," 1940, no. 306.

REFERENCES: Henri Leman, in *Les Beaux-Arts,* 1927, no. 89, pl. LIV; *Pennsylvania Museum Bulletin,* XXVII, 1932, p. 104; [Georg Swarzenski], *Arts of the Middle Ages* (exhibition catalogue), Boston, 1940, p. 86; no. 306, pl. LXVII; Günter Gall, in *Bulletin, Philadelphia Museum of Art,* July-September, 1967, pp. 260-275, ill.

Lent by the Philadelphia Museum of Art,
Given in memory of Thomas Dolan
and Sarah Brooke Dolan by their sons,
Thomas J. Dolan, Clarence W. Dolan and H. Yale Dolan, 30-1-89

PLATE VII

93   FRANCE, late 14th century

*Minne-Casket*

Hammered and incised metal and red-lacquered beechwood, H. 2-3/4 inches  (7.0 cm.), W. 5-1/2 inches  (14.0 cm.), D. 4-1/2 inches  (11.4 cm.)

Small coffrets made of metal, or of leather or fine woods decorated with metal fittings and ornaments, were usually given to the beloved at New Year's and bore inscriptions such as the one on this unusual example in beechwood. The *mon♡aves* is the same in medieval French dialect as *mon coeur à vous.* Straps of metal ornamented with roses and *fleurs-de-lis,* together with six-pointed stars in appliqué, form the relief decoration on the wood surface; at the corners and around the edge of the lid are metal guards with further decoration incised into the metal. The inscription is engraved in Gothic letters on a background of cross-hatched pattern.

EXHIBITIONS:  Tulsa, Oklahoma, Philbrook Art Center, "Medieval Art," 1965, no. 119; Ithaca, New York, Cornell University, Andrew Dickson White Museum of Art, "A Medieval Treasury," 1968, no. 78.

REFERENCES: *Medieval Art* (exhibition catalogue), Tulsa, 1965, no. 119; Robert G. Calkins, *A Medieval Treasury* (exhibition catalogue), Ithaca, 1968, p. 155, no. 78, ill.

PLATE VII                                        Lent by the Paul Drey Gallery, New York

94   FRANCO-FLEMISH, ca. 1375

*The Arrestation of Christ*

Translucent enamel on silver, Diam. 2-3/4 inches  (7.0 cm.)

During the second half of the fourteenth century and at the beginning of the fifteenth century enameled plaques such as this assumed an importance as products of courtly art that had been previously accorded to carved ivory plaques. Whether produced in Italy, Catalonia, the Rhineland, or in France, enameled plaques in either the *champlevé* or *bassetaille* technique are a characteristic and widespread phenomenon of the Later Middle Ages to which only random survival of examples can attest. Only in France, however, did the art achieve quite the high level that is displayed in this example. In practicing the technique of painting translucent colored enamels on plaques incised with the outlines and details of figures, the French goldsmiths were able to achieve as much freedom and depth in composition as could the best illuminators of manuscript miniatures. That the delicate enamels needed a base of either silver or gold to produce the effect of translucency explains the infrequent survival of examples of this art: the plaques were too susceptible to being melted down at a later date for their precious metals.

Here an artist of exceptional merit has transformed a traditional composition to fit the requirements of a round shape. Compositionally, the scene of Christ's betrayal keeps within bounds of two trees placed vertically to either side and curves outwards at top and bottom to fill up the space enclosed by the rim. Peter is shown meekly sheathing his sword after having rashly performed the amputation of Malchus' ear. The artist may have adhered to an artificial and merely elegant style of drapery, but his interest in differentiating between the bark of the two trees is in keeping with the most progressive style of Franco-Flemish illumination of the period. Philippe Verdier has suggested that the model was possibly a Parisian miniature in the Franco-Flemish style. Indeed, if one is to assume that this is but one from a series of enameled plaques illustrating the Passion of Christ, a manuscript model would seem likely.

EX COLLECTION: Lambert, Paris.

EXHIBITION: Baltimore, Walters Art Gallery, "The International Style," 1962, no. 130.

REFERENCES: [Philippe Verdier], in *The International Style* (exhibition catalogue), Baltimore, 1962, p. 128, no. 130, pl. CXVI; Colin Eisler, in *Art de France*, IV, 1964, p. 289.

PLATE XII                    Lent by Mr. and Mrs. Germain Seligman, New York

## 95  FRANCO-FLEMISH, late 14th century

*St. Michael Presenting a Donor to the Madonna and Child*

Silver plaque, H. 3-7/8 inches (9.9 cm.), W. 5 inches (2.7 cm.)

This exquisite engraved silver plaque is a rare example of late fourteenth-century goldsmith's art. Its style places it in the ambience of the Franco-Flemish artists who worked in the courtly circles of Charles VI, King of France, and of his uncles, Duke Philip the Bold of Burgundy, and Jean, Duc de Berry. The plaque recalls at once the double-page miniature in the *Très Belles Heures de Notre Dame*, illuminated by Jacquemart de Hesdin and his workshop for Jean de Berry ca. 1390-1395. Like the Duc de Berry in that miniature, the donor here kneels before the enthroned Virgin and is presented by his patron saint, St. Michael. In both the plaque and the miniature the donor is viewed in strict profile, in adherence to the Italian style of portrait fashionable at the time. The left edge of the throne in the plaque serves to divide the total area in half and thus properly removes the donor from the immediate aura of the Holy Mother and Infant. A string of rosary beads hangs from the donor's praying hands as he speaks the opening words of the rosary (engraved on the scroll): *ave maria gloria tua per sufragia solua clemencia nostro [plena] i gratia*. A book is on the floor beside him.

The heavy drapery covering the Madonna's knees, the elaborate throne which emphasizes receding lines, and the extension of the floor pavement to an imaginary wall behind the donor and his patron saint are indications of a concern for truth to the bulk of the figure and for understandable space relationships. Jacquemart de Hesdin's double-page miniature can be called the most progressive work of its time in striving for these effects. The principal difference in the interpretation of space between it and the present plaque is that in the left half of Jacquemart's representation a frame arbitrarily cuts off parts of the figures at the sides, giving the illusion that we are looking through a window onto what is only part of the actual space, whereas in the plaque the artist uses the less progressive means of suggesting depth by extending the right and upper edges of the throne, part of the scroll, the cross of St. Michael's cross-staff, and parts of his drapery *outside* the rosette frame.

For all this master's adeptness at presenting some of the best stylistic innovations of his time, he nevertheless denies himself the use of the most revolutionary of them all. Yet it is precisely this device of implying further space beyond three sides of the frame that would have turned his work into a mere imitation in metal of an illusionistic painted surface. By seeming to raise the throne and figures off a ground bordered by the rosette frame, he was respecting the integrity of the metal as a flat surface to be "sculpted." The technique employed for this "miniature relief sculpture" is that of first incising the metal with the outlines of the figures and then sculpting the contours of the parts enclosed by the outline. The subtlety of this technique and the illusionistic effects it produces can be readily seen in the profile head of the donor, in the relationship of the Virgin's hair to her face, and in the body of the Chirst Child. The plasticity in the figures goes far beyond what is called for in fulfillment of the decorative function of the plaque.

Philippe Verdier (in an undated letter) has called the plaque "a masterpiece of the goldsmith art of the late fourteenth century." He is inclined to ascribe the work to Hennequin du Vivier, goldsmith to Charles V, Charles VI, and Philip the Bold. Hennequin, whose only surviving work is supposedly the scepter of Charles V in the Louvre, was so highly regarded at the French court that on the visit to Paris of Karl IV, Emperor of Germany and Bohemia, the goldsmith was presented to the Emperor. This was only after Charles V, King of France, had presented the imperial visitor with gifts of goldsmith's work made by Hennequin.

In the scene represented on the plaque, the Virgin is seated on a throne hung with a cloth of honor and decorated with six-pointed stars that symbolize the lineage of the Virgin in the House of David. The Christ Child holds a violet which symbolizes His later Passion and suffering. Originally the cloth of honor and the rosette border, and perhaps the pavement and other details of the throne, may have been intended to receive translucent enamel. Perhaps the rest would have been gilded. An almost identical silver plaque formerly in the Garnier Collection and now in the Louvre (cf. Émile Molinier, Roger-Marx and Frantz Marcou, *L'Art français des origines à la fin du 19. siècle* [exhibition catalogue], Universial Exposition, Paris, 1900, pl. 32, 3) reportedly has traces of gilding (I am indebted to Marilyn Stokstad of the History of Art Department at the University of Kansas for this information). In composition, style of the figures, technique of incising, use of the ornamental rosettes and probably other decoration, the plaque with "St. Michael Presenting a Donor to the Madonna and Child" represents the high quality courtly productions in the Franco-Flemish style of the Parisian goldsmiths approaching 1400.

EX COLLECTION: Lanna, Prague.

REFERENCES: *Die Sammlung Lanna* (catalogue), no. 466, pl. XXXI; *Register* of the Museum of Art, University of Kansas, Lawrence, II, no. 2, p. 36, ill.; University of Kansas Museum of Art *Handbook,* Lawrence, 1962, p. 24, ill.; Marilyn Stokstad, *The Medieval Collections of the Museum of Art,* University of Kansas, Lawrence, 1963, no. 48, p. 20, ill.

PLATE IX

The University of Kansas Museum of Art, Gift of the Friends of the Museum, 59.05

96  SOUTH NETHERLANDS or EASTERN FRANCE (Lorraine), ca. 1400

*Aquamanile representing Aristotle ridden by Phyllis*

Bronze, H. 13-3/16 inches (33.5 cm.)

Often in the history of art the worker in bronze and other metals has claimed for himself a place of distinction and has led in artistic innovation. For a metalworker of ca. 1400 to achieve results of near comparable importance to the epoch-making ones in painting and monumental sculpture in stone of the time, however, is more than is to be expected. Yet the creator of the model from which this secular bronze *aquamanile* was cast has made just such a contribution. Here, for the first time in a small metal object of functional use two figures are uniquely combined in an arrangement which tells a story. Previously North German artists had fashioned *aquamanilia* representing the figure of a knight riding horseback or a mounted nobleman with a falcon (cf. the examples in *The Lehman Collection* [exhibition catalogue], Cincinnati, 1959, nos. 465-466), but an *aquamanile* which transcends the category of decorative conversation-piece by using the figures to narrate an episode from classical lore which had been transmitted through Medieval written sources, is to be regarded as truly exceptional. Set on the banquet table of a nobleman, the work would literally have "performed," both in the sense of functioning as a dispenser and of entertaining those seated at the table.

The story of how the philosopher and sage Aristotle was easily humiliated by women, particularly his pupil's, Alexander the Great's mistress, Campaspe, was a favorite of the Later Middle Ages, and was popularized by Henri d' Andely's *Lai d' Aristote.* Beginning with the time of Gottfried von Strassburg's *Tristram and Iseult*, in the thirteenth century, Campaspe was commonly known as Phyllis. Here Aristotle is represented in the traditional manner, ridden by Phyllis, but without being harnessed and whipped as in the work in which this medieval tradition culminates, Lucas van Leyden's famous undated woodcut (for literature on the iconography of Phyllis and Aristotle, see George Szabo, 1969, p. 361, n. 35).

Carmen Gómez-Moreno refers to a somewhat different Phyllis and Aristotle *aquamanile* in Brussels, which is thought to have been made in the Mosan region about the same time as the present example (see *Medieval Art from Private Collections* [exhibition catalogue], New York, 1968, no. 110). More recently, an *aquamanile* almost identical to the present one and preserved in the Musée Dovrée in Nantes was published by George Szabo (in *Apollo,* LXXXIX, 1969, p. 360, ill. p. 359). Szabo attributes the Nantes example to Burgundy, end of the fourteenth or beginning of the fifteenth century, and cites still another presumably related piece formerly belonging with the famous Basilewsky ivory situla to the same collection. The piece exhibited differs from the Nantes *aquamanile* only in that it shows Phyllis with slightly thicker arms and long, scalloped sleeves; also, in that it renders the locks of Aristotle's hair and certain details of his costume differently. The present example appears to be the more finely executed, and it has the additional interest of a small silhouetted rooster or cock mounted as a turn-handle on the spigot. Commonly referred to in German as a *Hahn,* and less frequently as a *coq* in French, it affords a visual play on words that becomes more vulgar in the later Dürer print of "The Men's Bath" (see Erwin Panofsky, *Albrecht Dürer,* Princeton, 1945, II, p. 42, no. 348).

EX COLLECTION: Chabières-Arlès.

EXHIBITIONS: Paris, Palais des Beaux-Arts, "Exposition retrospective de l'art français," 1900; Paris, Musée de l'Orangerie, "La Collection Lehman de New York," 1957, no. 185; Cincinnati Art Museum, "The Lehman Collection, New York," 1959, no. 468; New York, Metropolitan Museum of Art (Cloisters) "Medieval Art from Private Collections," no. 110.

REFERENCES: Jean Giraud, *Les arts du métal,* Paris, 1881, pl. XIII, no. 1; Victor Gay, *Glossaire archéologique,* Paris, 1887, I, p. 40, ill.; Gaston Migeon, *L'Exposition retrospective de l'art français,* Paris [1901], I, p. 8, ill.; Heinrich Reifferscheid, in *Mitteilungen aus dem germanischen Nationalmuseum,* 1912, p. 30; Otto von Falke, in *Pantheon,* II, 1928, pp. 563 ff.; O. von Falke and Erich Meyer, *Romanische Leuchter und Gefässe,* Berlin, 1935, p. 90, fig. 547; *Reallexikon zur deutschen Kunstgeschichte,* Stuttgart, 1937–, I, col. 1030, fig. 2, col. 1033; [Olga Raggio], in *La Collection Lehman de New York* (exhibition catalogue), Paris, 1957, no. 185, pl. LXXXIII; *The Lehman Collection, New York* (exhibition catalogue), Cincinnati, 1959, p. 38, no. 468, ill.; Carmen Gómez-Moreno, *Medieval Art from Private Collections* (exhibition catalogue), New York, 1968, no. 110, ill.; George Szabo, in *Apollo,* LXXXIX, 1969, p. 360, ill. p. 369.

PLATE VI                                       Lent by The Lehman Collection, New York

*Kneeling Prophet*

Gilt bronze, H. 5-1/2 inches (14.0 cm.), W. 3-1/2 inches (8.9 cm.) at widest point

The art of Northern Europe around 1400 reveals its fascination with the opportunities that series of Prophet figures offer for experimenting with drapery forms, especially in sculpture. Whether one views André Beauneveu's illuminations in the Psalter for the Duc de Berry or the sculptures from his workshop at Bourges, the statues for the porch of the Old Town Hall in Brussels connected with Claus Sluter's visit there or his later consoles for the chapel portal at the Chartreuse de Champmol near Dijon, or the console for the figure of St. Peter inside the Cathedral at Regensburg which is connected with the Peter Parler workshop at Prague, one witnesses a statement in this vein by or connected with a major artist of the time. The same applies to the "Kneeling Prophet" displayed here. The artist has organized the profuse drapery in a manner that complements his figure's balance and suggested movement, while making the spectator conscious of the weight borne by the two forearms and settled around the legs; the massive turban further serves to suggest volume and weight. The gentle flow of drapery lines across the chest, together with the streaming beard and the positions of the legs, endow the figure with an awakened spirit denoting his immediate response to prophetic vision. His eyes are fixed in a gaze that suggests a state of revelation, and his parted lips silently announce that he is about to speak.

Another kneeling Prophet figure of the same style and corresponding to our figure in material, gilded surface, and dimension, has been known ever since it was given to the Louvre in 1903 by Jules Maciet (cf. *Europäische Kunst um 1400* [exhibition catalogue], Vienna, 1960, pp. 287-288, no. 362, fig. 73), and has been previously ascribed to a follower of André Beauneveu. The former owner of our figure was the first to make the association with the Louvre figure, just before Theodor Müller was to characterize the Louvre example, the only one known to him, with the words, "The most telling testimony to the parallelism of growth of sculpture of metal in the Southern Netherlands, and monumental sculpture in stone in the style of the prophets from the portal of the Old Town Hall at Brussels, is the small gilt bronze figure of a kneeling prophet in the Louvre" (*Sculpture in the Netherlands, France, and Spain, 1400-1500*, Harmondsworth, 1966, p. 25). In the same year as Müller's reassessment of the Louvre Prophet, William Wixom brought the present figure to light, noting that the two gilt bronze figures show more restraint and control, more subtlety in achieving monumentality, than the figures of about 1380 from the *Beffroi* at Brussels. He places them in the middle of a line of development from the Brussels Prophets to Sluter's masterful consoles on the Chartreuse de Champmol portal. It is an intriguing idea that Sluter may have executed objects in the metalwork medium, but in the case of the small gilt bronze Prophets it is only possible to say that they may have been produced under his immediate influence. The question now arises as to whether they were produced in the South Netherlands or in France, for Sluter was established at the Court of Philip the Bold in Dijon from 1389. It is well known to what degree the rich and powerful Philip directed the wealth and artistic resources available to him to the adornment of the Carthusian monastery he had founded at Champmol in 1383, and it is not inconceivable that even before Sluter finished the portal sculpture in 1397 either a crucifix or a Calvary group supported by kneeling Prophets of gilt bronze stood on the main altar inside the Ducal Chapel, while outside on the monastery grounds Sluter's most monumental work, the *Well of Moses* with its six life-size Prophets surrounding the socle that supported the Calvary group, was already being erected. For the completion of the latter, Hannequin de Hacht was on hand to fashion a pair of gilded brass glasses to place on Jeremiah's nose.

It is true that the two bronze Prophets have recessions in their backs to receive the corners of a rectangular object and that they are of a proper size for supporting the base of a larger object. In addition, each of the Prophets held an opened scroll, as is evidenced by the hole for attachment in the Louvre figure's right hand and one in the present figure's right leg. Wixom contemplates a reconstruction approximating the *Moses Well* ensemble, which paraphrases a contemporary mystery play wherein the Prophets announce death verdicts for Christ despite the Virgin's anguished pleadings for mercy. It is possible that the same arrangement also was used for the alabaster sculptural ensemble of which three fragments, including a relief Prophet and a fragmentary *corpus*, are displayed in this exhibition (no. 47).

EX COLLECTION: [Herbert N. Bier, London].

EXHIBITIONS: The Cleveland Museum of Art, "Treasures from Medieval France," 1966-1967, no. VI-20.

LITERATURE: William Wixom, in Cleveland Museum of Art *Bulletin*, LIII, 1966, pp. 350-355, ill. cover and p. 352, figs. 8-10; *idem*, *Treasures from Medieval France*, Cleveland, 1967, pp. 4, 254, 376, no. VI-20, ill. p. 255; *idem*, in *Connoisseur*, VLXIVI, 1967, pp. 59, 61, fig. 7; Millard Meiss, *French Painting in the Time of Jean de Berry*, I, London, 1967, p. 386, n. 59; Philippe Verdier, in *L'Oeil*, nos. 164-165, 1968, p. 19, fig. 1.

PLATE XV

Lent by The Cleveland Museum of Art,
Purchase Leonard C. Hanna Jr. Bequest, 64.360

98   FRANCE, mid-15th century

*Chrismatory*

Engraved and parcel gilded copper, H. 7-1/2 inches (19.0 cm.)

This decorative object is most likely to have been used as a storage box for containing the holy oils used for annointment. It is designed as a hexagonally shaped tower raised on legs and is provided with a hasp. The walls are engraved with a pattern simulating stones laid with mortar, the surface of the peaked roof with a pattern of tiles. Around the upper edge of the walls runs a continuous band of crenellation to which the hinges are directly attached. On three of the walls are engraved standing figures in elaborate architectural settings representing the Virgin Mary, St. John, and St. Peter. The style of the figures and the technique of engraving suggests a date of roughly 1440-1450. According to Marie-Madeleine Gauthier (in an oral communication of May 15, 1967), the chrismatory, until now thought to be a pyx, was possibly made in Picardie. The ball of crystal glass on top probably is original.

EX COLLECTION: [Adolph Loewi, Los Angeles.]

REFERENCES: Marilyn Stokstad, *The Medieval Collections of the Museum of Art*, Lawrence, Kansas, 1963, no. 47, p. 19, as "ca. 1400."

PLATE LIV

The University of Kansas Museum of Art, 55.41

99   SOUTH NETHERLANDS, second half of the 15th century

*St. Adrian*

Cast and chased brass or light bronze, H. 12-1/8 inches (30.8 cm.)

This standing St. Adrian is one of four cast figures of male saints now in the same collection. The other three represent St. Peter, St. John, and St. Stephen and are of the same height, technique, and style; the discovery of more figures from the same series would not be too great a surprise. So far, instead of towns, only two rivers—Moselle and Meuse—have been mentioned as areas where they might have been produced. The latter, and the more likely of these two, could mean anywhere in the provinces of Limburg, Liège, and Namur, not to mention northern France. Dinant in Namur is noted for its bronze casting, but the bronzes thought to have been made there in general only aspire to the quality of St. Adrian and his companions. The polygonal base suggests more a Brabantine center like Malines or Brussels and a setting like one of the monumental lecterns or candelabra that were produced in Brabantine foundries and placed in churches throughout the region known today as Belgium. A quite similar, though more provincial piece, again with polygonal base, is the "Madonna and Child with the Rosary" in the Walters Art Gallery in Baltimore, thought to have been made in Malines (cf. Robert G. Calkins, *A Medieval Treasury* [exhibition catalogue], Ithaca, 1968, p. 167, no. 94, ill.). Closer in quality, of almost exactly the same size, and not dissimilar in style is the St. Leonard on the great paschal candelabrum in the Church of Saint-Léonard in Léau, the only authenticated work of the famous metal caster Renier van Thienen (cf. [Lucie Ninane], in *Flanders in the Fifteenth Century* [exhibition catalogue], Detroit, 1960, pp. 268-271, nos. 103-104, ill.). A more definite attribution could be made only if our St. Adrian and the matching figures could be associated with a large lectern or candelabrum for which documents exist, for, as J. Squilbeck has pointed out (in *Bruxelles au XV^e siècle* [exhibition catalogue], Brussels, 1953, p. 269), as many as twenty-five masters were on the register of the guild of metalworkers in late fifteenth-century Brussels alone.

The style of St. Adrian is characterized by the preference for broad, smooth surfaces giving cubic bulk to the figure and its individual parts—the whole figure echoes the shape of the anvil St. Adrian is holding. The face is given a planar treatment accentuating the forms of the jaws. The nose is straight and flat, and the mouth is relatively small. The excellent chasing has resulted in a smooth blending of parts, in mellow transitions. It is a figure of monumental bearing and forthright presentation.

EX COLLECTION: Campe, Hamburg; J. Pierpont Morgan, New York; Goodhart, New York.

EXHIBITIONS: Paris, Musée de 'Orangerie, "*La Collection Lehman de New York,*" 1957, no. 187; Cincinnati Art Museum, "The Lehman Collection, New York," 1959, no. 470; Montreal Museum of Fine Arts, "Images of the Saints. L'art et les saints," 1965, no. 31.

REFERENCES: *La Collection Lehman de New York* (exhibition catalogue), Paris, 1957, p. 123, no. 187, ill.; *The Lehman Collection, New York* (exhibition catalogue), Cincinnati, 1959, p. 38, no. 470, ill.; *Images of the Saints. L'art et les saints* (exhibition catalogue), Montreal, 1965, no. 31.

PLATE XLV                                    Lent by The Lehman Collection, New York

100    SOUTH NETHERLANDS, 15th century

*Madonna and Child*

Bronze, H. 26-3/4 inches (68.0 cm.), W. 9-11/16 inches (24.6 cm.), D. 9 inches (22.9 cm.)

Bronzes of this size are very unusual for the fifteenth-century Netherlands. The brass figures finished for the *Tomb of Isabella of Bourbon,* first wife of Charles the Bold and Duchess of Burgundy (d. 1465) are several inches shorter (cf. *Flanders in the Fifteenth Century* [exhibition catalogue], Detroit, 1960, pp. 264-

267, nos. 101-102, ill.). Other Flemish and Brabantine figures of bronze or brass made for the decoration of large lecterns are even smaller. Because of the lack of comparable examples on such a monumental scale, the temptation has often been to associate this work with Cologne or lower Rhenish production, as did Georg Swarzenski when he saw it. But the fine detail and finish given the piece distinguish it from lower Rhenish bronzes and point to one of the centers of bronze casting in Brabant or Flanders. Erich Meyer (in a letter to the Worcester Museum, dated September 1, 1951) sees a Flemish origin for the work and reasons that it shows less provincialism and primitivity than Rhenish bronzes from the same period.

EX COLLECTION: Richard von Kaufmann, Berlin; Karl von Weinberg, Waldfried, near Frankfurt; Baron Richard von Szilvinyi; [Wilhelm Heinrich, Frankfurt].

EXHIBITIONS: Berlin, Kunstgeschichtliche Gesellschaft, "Ausstellung von Kunstwerken des Mittelalters und der Renaissance aus Berliner Privatbesitz," 1898, no. 425.

REFERENCES: W. Bode and R. Stettiner, *Ausstellung von Kunstwerken des Mittelalters und der Renaissance aus Berliner Privatbesitz . . .* (exhibition catalogue), Berlin, 1899, p. 78, no. 425; Max J. Friedländer, F. Goldschmidt and Otto von Falke, *Die Sammlung Richard von Kaufmann*, Berlin, 1917, III, p. 26, no. 525, pl. 22; T.-B. in *Burlington Magazine*, XXXII (1918), p. 37, no. 252; Worcester Art Museum *News Bulletin and Calendar*, XVII, October, 1951, pp. 1-2, ill.

Lent by the Worcester Art Museum,
Worcester, Massachusetts, 1951.33

PLATE XXV

101    TOURNAI, second half of the 15th century

*St. Sebastian*

Lead, H. 4-1/8 inches (10.4 cm.), without base

Physical evidence suggests alone that this small figure was created as a model for use in a goldsmith's workshop. The back has a long groove channeled out and preserves the roughly incised lines that define the forms of the shoulders and upper legs. Although there are no arrows penetrating the body, the arms placed behind the figure (there are no hands) and the channel in the back providing a way of attaching the figure to a vertical shaft, probably a tree, clearly indicate that this is St. Sebastian.

Fortunately, the piece of goldsmith's work for which this served as a model is still preserved. It is a silver figure of St. Sebastian placed against a tree under an elaborate Gothic canopy supported by four spiraling columns, used to decorate what probably was the Bishop's crosier of the Church of St. Peter in Tournai. Formerly in the collection of Emil Weinberger in Vienna (sale catalogue of the Emil Weinberger Collection at Schwarzenberg Palace, Vienna, October, 1929, no. 127, p. 28, ill. under nos. 167 and 183 in error), the finished work is inscribed on the circular base with the words +*Eccles. S. Petri. Tornici.* and bears the arms of the city of Tournai. The silver is gilded except for the figure of St. Sebastian. In his left chest and left leg, upper right arm and right hip, are planted arrows. The silver figure corresponds in every detail with the present example, except for the arrows. Because of the presence of the tree it was unnecessary to complete the hands.

EX COLLECTION: Dr. Hugo Oelze, Amsterdam.

EXHIBITIONS: Hamburg, Museum für Kunst und Gewerbe Hamburg, "Sechs Sammler stellen aus," 1961, no. 12.

83

REFERENCES: *Sechs Sammler stellen aus* (exhibition catalogue), Hamburg, 1961, p. 8, no. 12.

PLATE XLIV                                  Lent by Edward R. Lubin, Inc., New York

102   FLANDERS, third quarter of the 15th century

*Half-figure of the Virgin*

Brass, silhouetted, H. 3-3/8 inches (8.6 cm.), W. 2 inches (5.0 cm.)

This small brass relief representing the Virgin Mary is of masterful design and fine execution. So far as is known, it is virtually without parallel in fifteenth-century Flemish art. Although the thin metal background against which the figure was silhouetted is cut away, there is evidence that it was conceived as a half-figure from the beginning. The surviving portion of the plaque needs some interpretation, for it is evident from the sorrowful Virgin's intense gaze to the left, and from the fact that the left corner has been cut off, that there was originally more of the composition to the left. Since the plaque must have been produced as a small object for private devotion it probably incorporated a figure of Christ with the Virgin of Piety. It could have been a half-figure image of the Passion Christ, as Middeldorf and Goetz suggested, except that the Virgin's hand attitudes, not being those of the usual *Mater Dolorosa,* imply a more narrative treatment of a Passion scene. Perhaps it was the upper body of the dead Christ supported by St. John that was represented in the missing portion.

Middeldorf and Goetz cite the influence of Dirc Bouts and parallels with contemporary Flemish painting, but it is easy to see our plaque as but a tiny reflection of the more monumental art of sculpture that was practiced by artists in the same guild to which the painters belonged in fifteenth-century Flanders. Perhaps the rarest surviving examples of that art, ranking with the best paintings from the third quarter of the century, are the Mourning Virgin from a Crucifixion group in the style of Roger van der Weyden, now in the Berlin Museum (cf. Theodor Müller, *Sculpture in the Netherlands, Germany, France, and Spain, 1400-1500,* Harmondsworth, 1966, fig. 104A) and the St. John companion piece to this, recently discovered in a private collection.

EXHIBITIONS: Art Institute of Chicago, "Medals and Plaquettes from the Sigmund Morgenroth Collection," 1944, no. 420.

REFERENCES: Ulrich Middeldorf and Oswald Goetz, *Medals and Plaquettes from the Sigmund Morgenroth Collection* (exhibition catalogue), Chicago, 1944, p. 58, no. 420, pl. XXV.

PLATE XLIV                    Lent by the Art Galleries, University of California, Santa Barbara, Sigmund Morgenroth Collection

103   FRANCE or FLANDERS, ca. 1466/67-1477

*Knife and Sharpener in leather case with arms and mottoes of the Dukes of Burgundy*

Knife, 15-5/16 inches (38.4 cm.); Sharpener, 9-5/16 inches (23.7 cm.); Sheath, 12-11/16 inches (32.3 cm.)

Upon the death of Philip the Good in 1467, Charles the Bold, his son, succeeded to the Duchy of Burgundy and the County of Flanders. Charles (1433-1477), like his father, patronized the arts and in fact is believed to have ordered the gold reliquary now in the Cathedral of Saint-Paul in Liège, immediately upon the death of Philip (cf. *Flanders in the Fifteenth Century* [exhibition catalogue], Detroit, 1960, pp. 298-300, no. 133, ill.). This knife and sharpener in an embossed leather case was made for Charles and bears his personal motto, *Je l'ay emprins,* on an engraved scroll on one side of the gilded metal pommel of the hilt. On the opposite side from the scroll are displayed the arms of Burgundy in *champlevé* enamel; other mottoes of the Dukes of Burgundy, including the *aultre* of *plus aultre,* appear on the knife handle and leather case. The form of the gilded pommel of the sharpener is that of the *briquet* engraved with a stone and flames, the insignia of the Order of the Golden Fleece. The *briquet* and stones are represented again on a field of flames on the knife pommel, on one side of the leather case, and on the knife blade. Decorating other parts of the case, knife hilt and blade are the thistle and the rose, the two flowers adopted by the Burgundian dukes. The blade is shaped for practical use, which indicates that this knife, like those of the Emperor Maximilian I that have been preserved, was used for hunting. An unidentifiable maker's mark appears on one side of the blade. The cord and tassels are modern.

EX COLLECTION: Baron Max von Goldschmidt-Rothschild, Frankfurt-am-Main.

PLATE XXXVI

Lent by The Metropolitan Museum of Art, New York, Rogers Fund, 50.119

104   FLANDERS, ca. 1480

*Pendant with figure of St. Sebastian*

Silver-gilt, H. 2-5/16 inches (6.0 cm.), W. 1-3/8 inches (3.7 cm.)

Saint Sebastian was venerated as one of the most important auxiliary saints and was often invoked against the plague. Besides, he was frequently the patron saint of archers' guilds because he had suffered his martyrdom by being shot with arrows. Hans Memling's painting, the "Martyrdom of St. Sebastian," of the early 1470's (Brussels, Musees Royaux), may be associated with an altarpiece donated by an archers' guild that would be roughly contemporary with this pendant of gilded silver. The pendant, in fact, may have been worn as an emblem by a member of such a guild, or perhaps it was ordered in connection with an archers' contest or some other specific event.

EX COLLECTION: [Blumka Gallery, New York].

PLATE XLIV

Lent by the Museum of Art, The Rhode Island School of Design, 48.334

105   FRANCE or FLANDERS, late 15th or early 16th century

*Reliquary with St. Barbara*

Gold and translucent enamel, H. 1-3/8 inches (3.5 cm.), W. 1-1/8 inches (2.8 cm.)

During the Later Middle Ages little distinction was made between *bona fide* reliquaries and ordinary pieces of jewelry; practically any piece of jewelry could be worn as *reliquière* or *reliquaire,* just as a *bona fide* reliquary could be used or worn as a *jocale* or *joyau* (see Erwin Panofsky, in *Essays in Honor of Georg Swarzenski,* Berlin, 1951, p. 76, n. 13). This late example of translucent enamel-work representing St. Barbara seated on a chair before a tower and reading from an opened book is mounted as a pendant in a gold frame of openwork decorated with enamelled flies alternating with thistles. It was once in the Spitzer Collection together with another translucent enamel of similar dimensions, technique and mounting, representing the "Lamentation over Christ" (now in a private collection in Chicago, without the frame). The figure and composition are reminiscent of miniatures of the late Ghent-Bruges School of manuscript illumination, as are the naturalistic motifs of the mountings. But the influence of Flemish works on French art around 1500 is very great, and the technique of painting with enamels on gold or silver surfaces to achieve translucency is a favorite one in France (see no. 94).

EX COLLECTION: Spitzer, Paris.

EXHIBITIONS: New York, Museum of Contemporary Crafts, "Enamels," 1959, no. 3.

REFERENCES: *La Collection Spitzer* (catalogue), Paris, III, 1891, p. 143, no. 9, pl. 1 (color); *Catalogue des objets d'art . . . Collection Spitzer* (sale catalogue), Paris, April 17-June 16, 1893, no. 1794; *Enamels* (exhibition catalogue), New York, 1959, no. 3.

PLATE LVIII

Lent by The Art Institute of Chicago, Mr. and Mrs. Martin A. Ryerson Collection, 38.1179

## NICOLAS LECLERC and JEAN de SAINT-PRIEST, Lyon, 1499

106 *Medal with Portrait of Louis XII*

107 *Medal with Portrait of Anne de Bretagne*

Bronze with traces of original gilding, Diam. 4-1/2 inches (11.4 cm.)

On January 8, 1499, a marriage took place between Louis XII, successor to Charles VIII, and Anne of Brittany. Anne, who was the widow of Charles VIII and by a curious set of circumstances Louis' mother-in-law, thereby became Queen of France for the second time and a wife for the third (she had been married by proxy to Maxmilian of Austria in 1490). Several months later the royal pair entered the city of Lyon in gala procession, the first visit the royal consort had paid the city since she and Charles were honored there in 1494. On her earlier visit a medal had been struck in commemoration of the event, and likewise for this second occasion, the first appearance of Louis of Orléans to the citizens of Lyon as King of France, a medal was struck. The medals on exhibition are cast with the portraits of Louis XII and his wife Anne, the obverse and reverse of the medal presented to the royal couple by the city of Lyon. A prancing lion, symbol of Lyon, is shown beneath each portrait bust. Louis XII is represented in profile against a field of *fleur-de-lis* of France surrounded by an inscription which reads: *FELICE. LVDOVICO. REGNA[N]TE. DVODECIMO. CESARE. ALTERO. GAVDET. OMNIS. NACIO.* ("Every nation rejoices under the reign of this second Caesar, the fortunate Louis XII"). The inscription around the profile bust portrait of Anne, who is shown against a divided field of *fleur-de-lis* and ermine tails of Brittany, makes reference to her earlier reign: *LVGDVN. REPVBLICA. GAVDETE. BIS. ANNA. REGNANTE. BENIGNE. SIC. FVI CONSLATA. 1499.* ("Amid the joy of the commonwealth of Lyon for the second time under the kindly reign of Anne, thus was I cast, 1499").

Numerous bronze casts of the medal exist, and the study of them is fraught with problems (cf. R. de Maulde La Clavière, in *Gazette des Beaux-Arts,* II, 1895, pp. 265-278, with bibliography and documents). The original medal given to Anne, cast of gold, no longer exists, but reportedly other examples in gold and silver still survive (see Stella Rubenstein-Bloch, 1926). Those in bronze exist in both double-face and uniface form and often vary in diameter as much as a few tenths of a centimeter, depending on how they are finished. Recently one of the double-face medals was acquired by the North Carolina Museum of Art (cf. M.-L. D'Otrange Mastai, in *The Connoisseur,* December, 1964, pp. 273-275, reprinted in North Carolina Museum of Art *Bulletin,* V, 1965, pp. 44-47); two uniface examples are presently owned by the dealer Michael Hall, of New York. The cast bronze medals also vary in degree and quality of technical finish. Usually, the most telling details are those of the two crowns, Anne's sleeve, and Louis' shirt collar. The ones on exhibition are very finely executed and show traces of original gilding. The existence of casts in gold, silver, and gilt-bronze suggests that not only did Louis and Anne receive a gold medal, but that other members of their retinue received them as well in silver and gilt-bronze according to their rank.

It is a documented fact that Nicolas Leclerc (active 1487-1507) and Jean de Saint-Priest (active 1490-1516), two sculptors of the city of Lyon, made the model, and that the medal was cast and finished by the goldsmiths Jean and Colin Lepère (cf. Natalis Rondot, *Les sculptures de Lyons,* 1884, p. 21). Beyond this, there is a tradition which holds that the painter Jean Perréal supplied the designs. This has been accepted by A. Armand (*Les médailleurs italiens des quinzième et seizième siècles,* 1883, II, p. 141, no. 12), Joseph Breck (1912, p. 54), L. Forrer (*Biographical Dictionary of Medalists,* 1909, IV, pp. 453, 454), Paul Ganz (*L'Oeuvre d'un amateur d'art, La Collection de F. Engel-Gros,* 1925, I, p. 356, no. 102), and Grete Ring (*A Century of French Painting, 1400-1500,* London, 1949, p. 189; *idem,* in *Burlington Magazine,* XCII, 1950, pp. 255-261). Recently, as part of much revision of the literature concerning Perréal, the attribution to him has been dropped (cf. M. Huillet d'Istria, in *Gazette des Beaux-Arts,* XL, 1952, pp. 57-63, 82-84). However, there remains no doubt that the portrait of Louis wearing the collar of the Order of St. Michael, and that of Anne de Bretagne wearing the Breton headdress, impressed on the Lyon medal, are among the most striking in the history of French portraiture. The medal belongs to the period of the early Renaissance in France, which began when Charles VIII returned from an expedition to Naples in 1495, accompanied by Italian artists and almost forty tons' weight of Italian works of art. At the same time the medal is usually considered the culmination of the late Medieval art of bronze casting (cf. *The French Bronze, 1500-1800* [exhibition catalogue], New York, 1968, no. 1).

REFERENCES: Joseph Breck, in Metropolitan Museum of Art *Bulletin,* VII, 1912, p. 54, ill. p. 52; *idem, Catalogue . . . of Sculpture,* Metropolitan Museum of Art, New York, 1913, no. 16; J. G. Phillips, in Metropolitan Museum of Art *Bulletin,* XXX, 1935, p. 199; Stella Rubenstein-Bloch, *The George and Florence Blumenthal Collection,* New York, 1926, II, pl. XLV.

Lent by The Metropolitan Museum of Art, New York,
Gift of George and Florence Blumenthal, 35.77;
PLATE LXVIII                                            and Hewitt Fund, 11.129.2

108   SOUTH NETHERLANDS, 15th century

*Badge with the Lion of Guelders* (?)

Gilded copper or brass and enamel, H. 1-3/4 inches (4.5 cm.), W. 1-1/2 inches (3.8 cm.)

A badge such as this was worn on the armor to identify the wearer's home. It would hang at an angle from the corner pierced with a hole, attached to the armor by a leather string. The lion rampant was the device of several counties and principalities, but the pale blue ground points to either Cleves or Guelders, more probably the latter.

EX COLLECTION: [Hendrichsz., Liège].

REFERENCES: Marilyn Stokstad, *The Medieval Collections of the Museum of Art,* University of Kansas, Lawrence, 1963, p. 21, no. 56.

PLATE XLV                         The University of Kansas Museum of Art, 59.54

109 FRANCE or FLANDERS, 15th century

*Arms of the City of Paris* (?)

Gilded copper and enamel, H. 3 inches (7.6 cm.), W. 2-3/4 inches (6.9 cm.)

Like the smaller enameled device on exhibition (no. 108), this probably served as a badge of identification. It is true that the armorial bearings are those of a locality rather than of a family, but the identification with Paris is questionable. The red field on which the ship is displayed may indicate some connection with Flanders.

EX COLLECTION: [Hendrichsz., Liège].

REFERENCES: Marilyn Stokstad, *The Medieval Collections of the Museum of Art*, University of Kansas, Lawrence, 1963, p. 21, no. 55.

PLATE XXXV                    The University of Kansas Museum of Art, 59.50

110 FRANCE (?), 15th century

*Decoration for horse trappings with fleur-de-lis*

Brass, H. 1-15/16 inches (4.9 cm.), W. 1-5/16 inches (3.3 cm.)

Decorations of metal, brightly enameled and gilded, were desirable in numbers for horse trappings not only for impressive appearances when the rider was in full regalia; they also attracted the ear by producing clinking noises while the horseman was riding. This one is fixed with a movable part in the shape of a *fleur-de-lis* in order to intensify the clinking of metal when it bounced. One must imagine both the visual and aural effect produced by an entire row of these on the horse's trappings. The ones that survive in greatest numbers from the late fourteenth and the fifteenth century seem to be Catalan; this example is as likely a candidate as any for a metal horse-trappings decoration made and used in France.

EX COLLECTION: Maurice de Talleyrand-Périgord, Duc de Dino, Paris.

REFERENCES: Baron C. A. de Cosson, *Le cabinet d'armes de Maurice de Talleyrand-Périgord, Duc de Dino*, Paris, 1901, pp. 107-108, no. M4.

Lent by The Metropolitan Museum of Art, New York, 04.3.375

FRANCE, 15th century

111 *Falconry badge*

Gilded copper and enamel, H. 1-1/2 inches (3.8 cm.), W. 7/8 inch (2.2 cm.)

112 *Falconry badge*

Gilded copper and enamel, H. 1 inch (2.5 cm.), W. 1-1/2 inches (3.8 cm.)

Brightly colored badges of metal emblazoned with the arms of nobles were as much a part of the gear for a falcon as they were for a horse during the Later Middle Ages (see no. 110). Helmut Nickel (in a letter dated September 3, 1969) reports he has been able to identify no. 111, with the armorial bearings gules, three pales vair, a chief or with a lambel azure, as the coat-of-arms of the Counts of Pol (for verification he cites Joseph Foster, *A Tudor Book of Arms*, DeWalden Library, n.d., p. 180, ill. p. 181; London, British Museum, Harley Ms. 6163, fol. 32 verso). The arms of the second example are bendy of six, gules and or, a bordure azure.

EX COLLECTION: Maurice de Talleyrand-Périgord, Duc de Dino, Paris.

REFERENCES: Baron C. A. de Cosson, *Le cabinet d'armes de Maurice de Talleyrand-Périgord, Duc de Dino*, Paris, 1901, pp. 107-108, no. M4.

Lent by The Metropolitan Museum of Art, New York, 04.3.370, 371

113 FRANCE, early 16th century

*Sword with the French royal arms and the inscription:* **MON IOIE—SAIN DENIS**

Steel and wood, etching and traces of gilding, H. 34-1/2 inches (86.3 cm.)

EX COLLECTION: Maurice de Talleyrand-Périgord, Duc de Dino, Paris.

REFERENCES: Baron C. A. de Cosson, *Le Cabinet d'armes de Maurice de Talleyrand-Périgord, Duc de Dino*, Paris, 1901, p. 56, no. F6.

Lent by The Metropolitan Museum of Art, New York, 04.3.28

114 DINANT, early 15th century

*Ewer*

Brass, H. 8 inches (20.3 cm.)

The term *dinanderie* has been extended to include Late Gothic objects of brass or bronze made in the Rhineland area of Germany and in others centers in Flanders, as well as in Dinant, the center in the bishopric of Liège, which led in this type of production. The making of wine ewers, basins, and various other objects, mainly for home use, was virtually the mainstay of the economy at Dinant, Malines, and other Netherlandish centers. This object of typical Dinant production probably served for pouring wine. Simple in design, it was first cast and then turned on a lathe to give it the horizontal raised and incised lines. The handle with the snail motif bridging it and the cover is characteristic for Dinant ewers of the early fifteenth century.

A similar example, without its original decoration on the cover, is in the collection of the Kunstgewerbemuseum in Berlin (Inv. no. 406, cf. *Kunstgewerbemuseum Berlin* (catalogue), no. 41, ill., with previous literature). Also, ewers very similar to the Kansas and Berlin examples are reproduced in J. F. von Hefner-Alteneck, *Trachten, Kunstwerke, Geräthschaften vom frühen Mittelalter bis zum Ende des 18. Jahrhunderts*, V, 1884, pl. 297g, and A. J. G. Verster, *Brons in de tijd*, 1956, no. 68, fig. 69.

EX COLLECTION: [Hofstätter, Vienna].

PLATE LVII                            University of Kansas Museum of Art, 55.90

115 DINANT, ca. 1425

*Ewer*

Bronze, H. 9-1/2 inches (24.1 cm.)

This is a utility object produced by the craftsmen in or near Dinant in the Netherlands and in some ways similar to the other example described above (no. 114). There is a similar aesthetic principle behind both—the smooth surfaces contrasting those broken by rings, the abstracted animal forms decorating the spout and handle, and a decorative motif on top of the lid. But in the present example there is more a disunity of parts stressed first by the narrowness of the neck and the gourd-like swelling of the belly. The spout, handle and lid decorations appear as separate entities added to the simple form of the container; the spout here definitely assumes the shape and features of a lion on whose back is raised a tiny projection that marks the place where in earlier examples the spout was attached to the neck by means of a strut. The motif crowning the lid is known in Flemish as *Kruisbloeme,* or literally "cross-flower," a popular decorative device for the ends of pinnacles in fifteenth-century architecture.

REFERENCES: M. H. De Young Memorial Museum *Catalogue,* San Francisco, 1966, p. (33), ill.

PLATE LVII

Lent by M. H. De Young Memorial Museum, San Francisco, Gift of E. and A. Silberman, 44.25

116   FRANCE, late 15th century

*Purse frame*

Iron, H. 7-1/2 inches (19.1 cm.), W. 5-5/8 inches (14.3 cm.)

Among the many objects for secular use made of iron in France and Flanders during the fifteenth century, frames to be sewn with pouches and worn at the belt as purses rank high as commodities. This one, missing its pouch, has an oval-shaped ring of hammered iron swinging from a decorative top that has first been cast and then pierced and worked with tools. The design incorporates a central motif resembling a façade of Gothic architecture, with an open arcade of three arches, buttressed on the ends. Underneath the arcade are fastened the cut-out Gothic letters *R* (or *P)* and *D,* probably the owner's initials. Earlier examples are often even more elaborate, consisting of two movable frame halves closing at the top with oranments in the form of walled castles flanked by lions, like the one formerly in the Figdor Collection (now in the Kunstgewerbemuseum in Berlin), which has letters forming the inscription *VIEN DE TESTRE* worked into the pierced decoration as one of its frame halves. Frames of a construction similar to the present example are also known (cf. Edgar B. Frank, in *Speculum,* XXIV, 1949, pp. 539-540, pl. XX, pl. 99; *idem, Old French Ironwork,* Cambridge, Mass., 1950, p. 184, pl. 76, no. 375, pl. 77, no. 376). One of the earliest representations of this type of belt-purse is on the Montferrand leather casket, exhibited here (no. 92).

EX COLLECTION: Mannheim.

REFERENCES: Catalogue of the Mannheim Collection, 1898, no. 227.

PLATE LXVII

Lent by The Metropolitan Museum of Art, New York, 17.190.374

117   FRANCE or FLANDERS, late 15th or early 16th century

*Bag for Game*

Frame of iron with pouch of velvet lined with silk, H. 6-3/8 inches (15.7 cm.), W. 8-1/2 inches (21.6 cm.) [frame]; D. 8 inches (20.3 cm.) [pouch]

This is an item similar to the purse frame also exhibited here (no. 116), except that its specific use was for bagging game, and its construction and the mechanism of the close are more complicated. The green velvet pouch (which is probably not original, but a later sixteenth- or seventeenth-century replacement), is sewn on a triple iron frame decorated with grotesque heads, acorns, and lizards, some of which slide in order to release the catch that keeps the upper pair of frames fastened. A third oval-shaped frame swings at the side holding a front pouch that can be opened by means of a drawstring. The repertory of *naturalia* is reminiscent of the border designs of the late Ghent-Bruges School of manuscript illumination, while the heads introduce a peculiar note in the design.

EX COLLECTION: Samuel Yellin, Philadelphia.

**PLATE LXXIII**

Lent by The Metropolitan Museum of Art, New York, 55.61.17

118    FRANCE, late 15th century

*Strongbox*

Iron, H. 5 inches (12.7 cm.), W. 6-3/4 inches (17.2 cm.), D. 10 inches (25.4 cm.)

Cassettes of this type are common among the skillfully designed and executed objects for secular use produced in the cruder metals in France during the fifteenth century. It is worked with great finesse in double layers of openwork tracery. The sides are given a rhythmic flow in the design in a manner that leads the eye across horizontally; the design of the lid is playful, giving the optical illusion that it changes (depending on whether one focuses on one or four squares at once). On either side of the lock are panels of *Fischblasenornament* similar to those on the chest lock shown in this exhibition (no. 119).

EX COLLECTION: Erwin Untermeyr, New York.

REFERENCES: Marilyn Stokstad, *The Medieval Collection of the Museum of Art,* The University of Kansas, Lawrence, 1963, p. 21, no. 58.

**PLATE LXVI**

The University of Kansas Museum of Art, Gift of Judge Erwin Untermeyr, 57.112

119    FRANCE, late 15th century

*Chest Lock with St. Michael and the Dragon*

Iron, H. 9-3/4 inches (24.3 cm.), W. 7-1/4 inches (18.1 cm.)

Locks of this type were produced in large numbers in France during the fifteenth century for large wooden floor chests. The most common type surviving is that which includes a projecting crown with *fleurs-de-lis* and a triple *fleur-de-lis* escutcheon beneath a single relief figure framed by panels of tracery and two piers with Gothic finials (cf. J. H. von Heffner-Alteneck, *Eisenwerke des Mittelalters,* II, 1885, for examples). This is an unusually fine example in terms of finish and relief figural decoration. It has four piers with Gothic finials, the two in the center incorporating elaborate twisted columns, and it has a canopy of unusually rich design and panels of tracery more complicated than the usual pattern called by the Germans *Fischblasenornament.* In place of a crown with *fleurs-de-lis* it has a second hanging canopy of open tracery under which one places the finger and pulls in order to release the hinge, which is the part surrounding St. Michael on three sides. The St. Michael and the Dragon is a sculpture on an intimate and miniature scale, the details of which are finely worked. It is hard to explain the keyholes in the right inset panel as anything but later alterations made to transform the piece into a doorlock, for the keyhole usually was hidden behind the hinged part at the bottom with the crown or canopy. The lock mechanism is missing, and the face came with a Renaissance key of later date.

REFERENCES: City Art Museum *Bulletin*, VIII, April-June, 1923; *Handbook of the City Art Museum of St. Louis*, St. Louis, (1953), ill. p. 50.

PLATE LXIV                           Lent by The City Art Museum of St. Louis, 141:21

120   TROYES, early 16th century

*Tabernacle Door with the Calvary*

Iron, H. 19 inches (48.2 cm.), W. 10-1/8 inches (35.8 cm.)

This elaborate work entirely of chiselled iron has the distinction of coming from one of the most celebrated abbeys in northern France, St.-Loup at Troyes, where it served as the door to the tabernacle for containing the Holy Sacrament. It may have been produced for the high altar during the office of the Abbé Nicolas Forjot of St.-Loup (1508-1512), who is shown kneeling next to the Virgin in a stone sculpture in the Hôtel-Dieu at Troyes. The design features a pierced background with intricate tracery up against which is mounted the heavy frame with a running motif on the inside composed of ribbon-wrapped tree branches probably symbolizing the Tree of Life. Separately are added the ornate canopies, the cross, and the figures. The Virgin and St. John are represented with halos of further elaborate design, and stand on consoles of pierced leaf ornament. A place is provided in the tracery to the left of the cross for inserting the key to a lock which is now missing.

The style of the figures agrees with that of other Champagne sculptures of the period, including the small votive sculpture included in this exhibition (no. 72). Catering to a bourgeois set of patrons, the art of Champagne glorifies the ordinary middle-class visage and simple costume in the figures and juxtaposes the middle-class dream of décor in super-abundance.

EX COLLECTION: Debruge Duménil, Paris; W. H. Forman, London; Henry Walters, Baltimore.

EXHIBITIONS: London, South Kensington Museum, 1862, no. 6635.

REFERENCES: Arnaud, *Voyage archéologique et pittoresque dans le département de l'Aube* [Troyes, 1837]; *Description des objets d'art qui composent la Collection Debruge Duménil*, introduction by Jules Labarte, Paris, 1847, p. 721, no. 1481 (auction in 1849 or 1850?).

PLATE LXV                           Lent by The Walters Art Gallery, Baltimore, 52.103

# EMBROIDERIES AND TAPESTRIES

121   FRANCE, early 15th century

*Orphrey from a Chasuble with the Crucifixion*

Linen embroidered with colored silk and gold thread, H. 41-1/2 inches (1.053 m.), W. 23-11/16 inches (.60 m.)

The art of embroidery was employed to a large degree in the decoration of secular costume during the Later Middle Ages, but unfortunately none of the examples for profane use have survived. What remain are but a tiny fraction of the total production of ecclesiastical vestments and altar cloths, and for the most part these survive only fragmentarily. Even the extant pieces with greatest artistic interest from around 1400 are largely German and Bohemian in origin. The problem confronted in localizing late fourteenth- and early fifteenth-century embroideries to France is that the designs were produced in close connection with the painters, and that what little is known of early fifteenth-century French painting is hotly debated and in part often ascribed to Bohemia. Thus, one cannot be certain that this fragmentary orphrey representing the "Crucifixion," with St. John comforting the Virgin beneath the cross and angels borne on stylized clouds and offering golden crowns to the Crucified Christ, was produced in France. Yet it is a fine example of the art as practiced at the two leading courts of Europe at the time, Paris and Prague. Pictorial embroideries such as this are the work of highly skilled artists whose occupation was known as "needle painting" *(peinture à l'aiguille)*. The demand was very great for artists skilled in the art of embroidery, and they were often as highly regarded as the manuscript illuminators and panel painters. But because they depended upon the painters for their designs, which were then probably used more than once, they were not apt to keep up with the latest stylistic innovations in other pictorial media.

The elegance of the courtly style is felt here in the complicated pattern of curvilinear lines of drapery in the Virgin and St. John figures and in the upward-curving arms of Christ. But the Crucified Christ possesses an inner strength that is lacking in the other figures and is accorded a more penetrating realism that bespeaks the influence brought upon French art by the Netherlandish artists who worked in France toward the end of the fourteenth century. Although the actual form of the *corpus* is more indicative of the direct influence of late fourteenth-century Italian art, particularly the swelling rib cage and the sharply delineated ribs, it is not unreasonable to compare the various heads, the hairstyles, and some of the drapery patterns to the famous *tondo* attributed to Jean Malouel in the Louvre. The checkered background is applied here in the conventional manner of late fourteenth- and early fifteenth-century French manuscript illuminators.

EX COLLECTION: Joseph Brummer, New York.

EXHIBITIONS: Boston, Museum of Fine Arts, "Arts of the Middle Ages," 1940, no. 108.

REFERENCES: [Georg Swarzenski], *Arts of the Middle Ages* (exhibition catalogue), Boston, 1940, p. 37, no. 108, ill.; sale catalogue of the Brummer Collection at Parke-Bernet Galleries, New York, April 1949; *Handbook of the City Art Museum of Saint Louis* (1953), ill. p. 46; City Art Museum *Bulletin*, Winter-Spring, 1950, ill.

PLATE XIII                    Lent by The City Art Museum of St. Louis, 76:49

122  FRANCO-FLEMISH, ca. 1430-1435

*St. Martin Bringing to Life a Dead Man*

Linen embroidered with silk, silver, and silver-gilt threads, Diam. 6-1/2 inches (16.5 cm.)

Thirty-two embroidered roundels illustrating with remarkable completeness the life of St. Martin of Tours form one of the most important examples of fifteenth-century embroiderer's art extant. This roundel is the eighth in sequence in the historiated series, most of which is remounted on orphreys preserved in the Musée Historique des Tissus in Lyon. The existence of several squarish embroidered panels with arched tops illustrating further scenes from St. Martin's life indicates that we have here to deal with the decorations for a "chapel," that is, a matched set of ecclesiastical vestments and cloth for adorning the altar, such as exists in the magnificent *Ornat* of the Order of the Golden Fleece now in the Schatzkammer of the Kunsthistorisches Museum in Vienna. Margaret Freeman attributes the design of this roundel to the first of five artists whose hands she separates in the series of roundels. She is tempted to connect this series with mention in De Laborde (*Les Ducs de Bourgogne*, I, p. 277, no. 979) of payment by Philip the Good of Burgundy for a set of chapel vestments and altar cloths to Thiery du Chastel, the Duke's master embroiderer. While this is only a tentative suggestion, it is likely, because of the traditional connection of St. Martin with vineyards and the appearance of Burgundian costume in the embroideries, that they were made for someone at the Burgundian court. Style relationships with early fifteenth-century manuscript miniatures are numerous, and particularly the dead corpse in this roundel recalls the famous miniature of "Mourning over the Body of Christ" from the *Hours of Rohan* in the Bibliothèque Nationale in Paris. The fact that the series densely illustrates the St. Martin legend, scene by scene, and the regular presence of checkered ground and backgrounds—the stock in trade of early fifteenth-century French miniaturists—makes it seem not too unlikely that the entire series derives from an illustrated text of the life of St. Martin. Illustrated saints' lives were extremely popular in the Later Middle Ages.

The embroidery technique displayed here involves laying down silver-gilt foil-covered silk threads on the linen background and attaching them by means of silk threads of different colors. These gold threads are referred to as *or de Chypre*. The present example is one of the few in the series that shows the original turning back of the gold thread at the outer edge of the circle. The drawn outlines of the figures are stitched in a dark color of thread and the interior is filled out in various colors of silk threads and in a variety of stitches, with the result that the finished embroidery has almost a painted appearance.

EX COLLECTION: Salvadori, Florence; Joseph Brummer, New York.

EXHIBITIONS: Boston, Museum of Fine Arts, "Arts of the Middle Ages," 1940, no. 113; New York, Metropolitan Museum of Art (Cloisters), 1968-1969, "Medieval Art from Private Collections," no. 204.

REFERENCES: [Georg Swarzenski], *Arts of the Middle Ages* (exhibition catalogue), Boston, 1940, no. 113; sale catalogue of the Brummer Collection at Parke-Bernet Galleries, New York, April 22, 1949, p. 129, no. 511; Colin Eisler, in *Burlington Magazine*, CIX, 1967, p. 577, fig. 41; Margaret B. Freeman, *The Saint Martin Embroideries*, New York, 1968, pp. 29, 68-69, 79, 82, 126, pl. VIII, fig. 30; Carmen Gómez-Moreno, *Medieval Art from Private Collections* (exhibition catalogue), New York, 1968, no. 204, ill.

PLATE XVII                                              Lent by The Lehman Collection, New York

123   FLANDERS, ca. 1440-1445

*St. Catherine in the Temple Arguing Against the Worship of Idols*

Linen embroidered with silk, silver and silver-gilt threads, Diam. 6-1/2 inches (16.5 cm.)

This is one of eight surviving embroidered roundels from what originally must have been a large cycle illustrating the life of St. Catherine. A second is exhibited here under number 124. All eight roundels are approximately the same size and their dimensions correspond to those of a different series illustrating scenes from the life of St. Martin, of which an example is also shown here (no. 122). Not only are the St. Catherine roundels perhaps as much as a decade later in date; they also differ from the St. Martin roundels in style and technique. While the St. Martin embroideries show stylistic parallels to the art of Parisian illuminators of the first quarter of the fifteenth century, the St. Catherine roundels take their keynote from the early Flemish panel painters, especially those of the school of Tournai. The Master of Flémalle (Robert Campin), Jacques Daret, and the younger Roger van der Weyden, all have been mentioned in connection with them, and certainly it is within this artistic milieu that the designs must have originated. Tournai, next to Arras, was the leading tapestry center of the time, so it is no wonder that technically the St. Catherine embroideries give somewhat the effect of the warp and weft of a tapestry instead of the *peinture à l'aiguille* effect more characteristic of the St. Martin embroideries. The silver-gilt foil-covered threads for the background are couched down in horizontal lines, while the stitches for the figures are made vertically. Whereas in the St. Martin embroideries one sees only the beginnings of a technique known as *or nué*, which involves spacing the colored silk threads used to couch down the gold threads in an uneven manner to produce a shimmering effect, the St. Catherine embroideries show this technique fully developed.

It would seem that in spite of their probable Flemish production, the St. Catherine embroidered roundels are somehow connected with Burgundy. An illustrated manuscript of the *Vie de Madame Sainte Katherine* with sixty miniatures from the workshop of William Vrelant, made for Duke Philip the Good of Burgundy (Paris, Bibliothèque Nationale, ms. fr. 6449), already has been shown by Margaret Freeman to have compositions almost identical to ones in the St. Catherine roundels. But one is easily persuaded to accept her conclusion that the embroidered compositions are not based on the manuscript miniatures, but rather that their original designs were used as models by Philip's miniaturists. Not only is it obvious that the French translation of the text for Philip's manuscript was completed by Jean Miélot only in 1457, long after the St. Catherine roundels were completed, but also one has to reckon with the dates of activity of William Vrelant and his workshop. Miss Freeman has suggested on separate occasions that both the St. Martin series and the St. Catherine series were produced for Philip the Good. But apparently no one has followed the existing evidence to the conclusion that the St. Catherine embroideries have been companion pieces to the St. Martin embroideries ever since they were produced. The roundels of both series have the same measurements in diameter, which since they were produced in different places would be unlikely were they to have been produced for anything but the same setting. Some of the roundels of each series were found mixed in seventeenth century remountings on two different chasubles, which would indicate that they had come from the same source. Furthermore, the central feature of the cross-shaped remountings just mentioned was in each case one of the arched-top square panels representing additional scenes from the life of St. Martin that are in the same style and technique as the St. Catherine roundels (cf. Margaret Freeman, *The Saint Martin Embroideries*, New York, 1968, pp. 93-107, pls. XXXIII-XXXVII). There remains no alternative but to suppose that some time after the St. Martin roundels were ordered in France, the same donor or the same institution for which these were made ordered from Flanders additional panels with scenes of St. Martin and a series of roundels with scenes of St. Catherine. And what more likely a candidate for their commission could there be than Duke Philip the Good, whose seat in Burgundy allowed him to draw on the best resources of both France and Flanders? The evidence submitted by Miss Freeman that Philip the Good had a special liking for St. Catherine, however enlightening, is less to the point than would be an investigation into the possibility that there may exist a principal Burgundian church dedicated to both St. Martin and St. Catherine. Multiple dedications were not uncommon during the Middle Ages, although one Saint usually took precedence over any additional dedications. Such an investigation may yet show where both the St. Martin and the St. Catherine embroideries were originally placed.

Our embroidery shows an early incident in the life of St. Catherine, one which takes place prior to her imprisonment. Besides the lithe golden figure of the pagan idol, of noteworthy interest are the two musicians, each of whom plays a different type of trumpet. One should note particularly the expressiveness in their hands, perhaps the best indication in this roundel of the extent to which embroidery in the fifteenth century was a major art. There appears to be no basis for Miss Freeman's comparison of the architecture in this roundel with that in a fresco representing a scene from the life of St. Catherine, executed in 1387 by Spinello Aretino in Antella, near Florence.

EX COLLECTION: M. Duponchel (?), Paris, 1919; Joseph Brummer, New York.

EXHIBITIONS: Musée de l'Orangerie, Paris, "La Collection Lehman de New York" 1957, no. 292; Cincinnati Art Museum, "The Lehman Collection, New York," 1958, no. 350.

REFERENCES: Margaret B. Freeman, in Metropolitan Museum of Art *Bulletin*, XIV, 1955, pp. 285, 289, ill. p. 286; *La Collection Lehman de New York* (exhibition catalogue), Paris, 1957, no. 292, p. 166; *The Lehman Collection, New York* (exhibition catalogue), Cincinnati, 1958, no. 350, p. 33; Margaret B. Freeman, *The St. Martin Embroideries,* New York, 1968, fig. 6.

PLATE XXVI                    Lent by The Lehman Collection, New York

124    FLANDERS, ca. 1440-1445

*The Meeting of the Queen and St. Catherine*

Linen embroidered with silk, silver, and silver-gilt threads, Diam. 6-1/2 inches (16.5 cm.)

Before it was discovered that this and another embroidered roundel included in this exhibition (no. 123) belonged to a series of roundels illustrating the life of St. Catherine, probably produced for an altar frontal or dorsal, the subject matter of this piece was described as "Four Court Ladies." That it is not a secular work does not detract from the interest it holds in showing the height of Burgundian fashion in costume during the second quarter of the fifteenth century. The scene is the arrival of the Queen to meet St. Catherine in prison after she has heard of St. Catherine's remarkable traits and cannot be kept away for curiosity's sake. This is the fourth in sequence of the eight surviving roundels from what must have been a much more extensive original cycle illustrating this popular saint's life. The style of the drapery is in full accord with that found in the works of Roger van der Weyden and his master, the Master of Flémalle (Robert Campin).

EX COLLECTION: M. Duponchel (?), Paris; Joseph Brummer, New York.

EXHIBITIONS: Boston, Museum of Fine Arts, "Arts of the Middle Ages," 1940.

REFERENCES: [Georg Swarzenski], *Arts of the Middle Ages* (exhibition catalogue), 1940, no. 114; Seattle Art Museum *Handbook,* 1951, p. 116; Margaret B. Freeman, in Metropolitan Museum of Art *Bulletin*, XIII, 1955, p. 287, ill. p. 291; *idem, The Saint Martin Embroideries,* New York, 1968, fig. 6.

                                              Lent by The Seattle Art Museum,
PLATE XXVI               Donald E. Fredericks Memorial Collection, 49.F40.1

125    TOURNAI, ca. 1490

*Parable of the Rich Young Man*

Tapestry, silk and wool, H. 6 feet 1 inch (1.86 m.), W. 5 feet 6 inches (1.68 m.)

The subject of this tapestry has been identified as deriving from the Biblical story of Lazarus, the beggar, and the rich young man who refused to share his worldly goods with him. According to this interpretation we see here the rich man, worldly goods at his feet, about to enter the fiery gates of Hell.

Whether this interpretation is correct (and it seems at least open to question inasmuch as Lazarus is nowhere to be seen) or whether the subject is simply a more generalized variant of the *memento mori* theme, the tapestry is of particular interest because of its intermingling of Christian moralism and classical mythology. Cerebrus, the three-headed guardian of the entrance to the underworld in classical myth, is shown here about to unlock the gate to Hades. The figure at the left, although perhaps only a personification of Death, may also represent Pluto, Greek god of the subterranean world of the dead.

EX COLLECTION: Alphonse Kann, Paris.

PLATE L                                        Lent by French & Co., Inc., New York

126   FRANCE, late 15th century

*Mille Fleurs Tapestry with a Pair of Lovers*

Tapestry, silk and wool, H. 8 feet 4 inches (2.54 m.), W. 8 feet 9 inches (2.67 m.)

This fine *mille fleurs* tapestry is believed to have been designed by Jean Rosimbo. Two equestrian figures, male and female, pass each other in opposite directions. The young man in red hose, wears a red and white tunic used with green and yellow over a blue and white shirt. He holds a plate of apples, while the young woman, dressed in a blue and red blouse with plain blue sleeves and a full, long red skirt, carries a bird.

The Latin inscription reads: *Que Gulerust equos rata prudencia vulta talis homs visitur sensibus illis et Racis D.* ("Who drives horses must have prudence, but the man with such feeling [of love] must have his full sense.") [Translated by Mr. Haracourt, former Director of The Cluny Museum, Paris.]

EX COLLECTION: William Randolph Hearst.

EXHIBITIONS: New York World's Fair, 1929.

REFERENCES: *The Compleat Collector,* 1943, III, no. 3, ill. (cover); [Warren Beach], *Fine Arts Gallery of San Diego Catalogue,* 1960, p. 115.

PLATE LXXIV                              Lent by the Fine Arts Society of San Diego

127   FRANCO-FLEMISH, late 15th century

*King Solomon and the Queen of Sheba*

Tapestry, silk and wool, H. 11 feet 7 inches (3.53 m.), W. 13 feet 5 inches (4.09 m.)

This tapestry, believed to have been woven in Brussels toward 1500, has been interpreted as depicting the Queen of Sheba appearing before King Solomon. The figure identified as Solomon stands at the right with a spear in his left hand and receives the Queen who kneels before him with her ladies-in-waiting. On either side are groups of court figures, and in the upper right is a group of trumpeters. All the figures are attired in richly brocaded material of the period.

A tapestry similar to this one in technique, style and subject was exhibited in Brussels in 1951 under the title of "Solomon and the Queen of Sheba" (cf. *Le Siècle de Bourgogne* [exhibition catalogue], Brussels, 1951, p. 68, no. 141, ill. pl. XLV). The traditional identification of the subject, however, was questioned and the suggestion made that it probably represents "a scene of justice from the Roman epoch."

PROVENANCE: From an unidentified Spanish cathedral.

**PLATE XLI**                                          Lent by French & Co., Inc., New York

128    BRUSSELS, ca. 1500

*Maximilian and Philip the Handsome*

Tapestry, silk and wool, H. 6 feet 5 inches (1.96 m.), W. 7 feet 6 inches (2.29 m.)

The central figures in this court scene are thought to represent the Emperor
Maximilian I and, standing before him, the youthful Philip the Handsome. It is
said that this tapestry was presented to the Cathedral of Saragossa by King
Ferdinand of Aragon (1452-1516), known as Ferdinand the Catholic, husband of
Queen Isabella and father-in-law of Philip. Philip, called the Handsome (1478-
1506), was the son of the Emperor Maximilian I and Mary of Burgundy, and was
born in Bruges; on the death of his mother in 1482 he inherited as a child the
domains of Burgundy, and was married in 1496 to Juana, the daughter of
Ferdinand and Isabella. He succeeded to the throne of Castile in 1504 as Philip
I of Spain, and died two years later.

PROVENANCE: Treasury of the Cathedral of Saragossa.

**PLATE LXXI**                                        Lent by French & Co., Inc., New York

129    FLANDERS, early 16th century

*Scenes from a Romance*

Tapestry, silk and wool, H. 12 feet 3 inches (3.74 m.), W. 12 feet 3 inches (3.74 m.)

The scene here illustrated probably derives from a contemporary romance of
chivalry related to the "Court of Love" tapestries popular at the time. A queen (?)
surrounded by her court apparently awaits the preparation of a document. In
the background, upper left, a knight is writing a letter, and on the opposite side
two knights wait on horseback.

The cartoon is said to have come from the shop of Maître Phillipe. Jean van
Room, whose signature appears on a similar tapestry of David and Bathsheba in
the former Royal Spanish Collection, is thought to have collaborated.

EX COLLECTION: Marquis of Casa-Torres, Madrid; Georges Hoentschel, Paris; J. Pierpont
Morgan, New York.

EXHIBITIONS: San Francisco Museum of Art, "Loan Exhibition of European Tapestries," 1922.

REFERENCES: *Collections Georges Hoentschel*, Paris, 1908, I, p. 33-35, pl. LXVIII, LXIX; P.
Ackerman, *Catalogue of an Exhibition of European Tapestries*, San Francisco, 1922.

**PLATE LXX**                                         Lent by French & Co., Inc., New York

130    FRANCO-FLEMISH

*Falcon Hunt*

Tapestry, silk and wool, H. 8 feet 1-1/2 inches (2.44 m.), W. 8 feet 8 inches (2.65 m.)

A young noble, richly clad, hunts with poised falcon in the lush growth of a
*mille-fleurs* forest. Accompanied by an admiring lady and followed by a servant
with halberd, he possesses all the accoutrements of a luxurious and privileged
courtly life. A leading tapestry-weaving center in France or Flanders supplied
this woven field, which exalts the isolated princely preserve.

EXHIBITIONS: Paris, Musée de l'Orangerie, *"La Collection Lehman de New York,"* 1957, no. 290; Cincinnati Art Museum, "The Lehman Collection, New York," 1959, no. 352.

REFERENCES: G. J. Demotte, *La tapisserie gothique,* 1922, p. 9, pl. CLXIII; G. L. Hunter, *The Practical Book of Tapestries,* 1925, p. 108; H. Göbel, *Wandteppiche,* II, *Die romanischen Länder,* 1928, Part 1, p. 280; *Collection Lehman de New York* (exhibition catalogue), Paris, 1957, p. 165; *The Lehman Collection, New York* (exhibition catalogue), Cincinnati, 1959, p. 33, no. 352, ill.

PLATE LXXIII                     Lent by The Lehman Collection, New York

131   FLANDERS, late 15th century

*Mercury*

Tapestry, silk and wool, H. 7 feet 3 inches (2.21 m.), W. 6 feet 10-3/4 inches (2.10 m.)

That classical lore arrived at the Later Middle Ages somewhat corrupted seems best illustrated by this Mercury, who summons up the classical image tattered and torn. While still sporting the classical attributes of winged hat, horn and purse, he is more costumed fool than smiling youth, a ragged, wrinkled man aided by a crude walking-stick and a pair of clumsy elevated sandals (instead of winged heels). This tapestry may, in fact, poke fun at hasty procedures and fly-by-night circumstances. Surely, the torn sack spilling money, broken water-flask, and splitting sword-sheath make this Mercury unfit to travel. The ruffled owl recalls the popular saying which survives in the German, "in der Eulenflucht," meaning "to be in a hurry," while the porcupine may illustrate the proverb, "er hat immer Igel zu bürsten," meaning "he needs to make haste." Glasses are given to one who is short-sighted, an idea which is conveyed in numerous Netherlandish and German proverbs. A latter-day Till Eulenspiegel or an ancestral Papageno, this Mercury, immersed in folklore, wants to amuse. The design and concept are worthy of a major artist of the time, a Quentin Metsys.

FRONTISPIECE                                    Lent anonymously

132   TOURNAI, early 16th century

*Sheep Shearing and Hunting*

Tapestry, silk and wool, H. 10 feet (3.1 m.), W. 14 feet 7 inches (4.45 m.)

This tapestry, one of a set of four representing rural pursuits and pastimes of assorted gentle folk and peasants, has been identified by Marvin Ross as a Tournai production and dated "about the second decade of the sixteenth century." At the upper center a mounted falconer extends his arm as if to retrieve a falcon which brings down a large goose or swan. In the center foreground a shepherdess prepares to shear a docile lamb, while at the right a shepherd proffers a leather collar. At the left a costumed jester approaches a young nobleman who pours wine from a flagon.

Ross endorses as "quite plausible" James Rorimer's suggestion that a figure in one of the other tapestries in the series, wearing a hat with red, white and tan plumes may be intended to represent Louis XII, who adopted those colors after his marriage to Anne of Brittany in 1499. If this identification is correct the tapestries would likely have been commissioned between that date and the time of Louis' death sixteen years later.

EX COLLECTION: W. A. Clark.

REFERENCES: *Illustrated Handbook of the William A. Clark Collection*, Corcoran Gallery of Art, Washington, D.C., 1932, p. 75; Marvin C. Ross, in Corcoran Gallery of Art *Bulletin*, IX, 2, 1957, p. 6, fig. 3.

PLATE LXXV

Lent by The Corcoran Gallery of Art,<br>Washington, D.C., W. A. Clark Collection

133  FRANCO-FLEMISH, first quarter of the 16th century

*Pastoral Scene with Bird-shooting*

Tapestry, silk and wool, H. 10 feet 6 inches (3.2 m.), W. 11 feet 3 inches (3.4 m.)

Like another approximately contemporary tapestry in this exhibition (no. 132) this is one of a set of four depicting outdoor activities of individuals from various classes of society. In both we see shepherds and shepherdesses, falconers and archers. Figures in the present tapestry, however, are rendered with somewhat less naturalism and considerably less detail. Comparison of the similarly posed figures in the lower right corners of both tapestries is revealing.

Calkins, in discussing another tapestry from this series (cf. *A Medieval Treasury* [exhibition catalogue], Ithaca, 1968, pp. 186-188, no. 114) suggests a symbolic meaning for the enclosed garden or park which appears in both works, speculating that it may be intended as an evocation of the Garden of Paradise or even as an oblique reference to the Immaculate Conception of the Virgin.

EX COLLECTION: Count de Vauguyon, Paris; George and Florence Blumenthal, New York.

REFERENCES: Stella Rubenstein-Bloch, *George and Florence Blumenthal Collection* (catalogue), 1927, IV, pl. VII, IX; Metropolitan Museum of Art, *Medieval Tapestries*, New York, 1947, fig. 18.

PLATE LXXVI

Lent by The Metropolitan Museum of Art,<br>Bequest of George Blumenthal, 41.190.228

# COINS, LETTERS AND DOCUMENTS

134  MALINES, 14th century

*Lion d'or of Wenzel of Luxembourg*

Gold Coin, Diam. 1-3/16 inches (3.0 cm.)

Lent by The Detroit Institute of Arts,<br>Gift of Dr. and Mrs. Irving F. Burton

135  LOUVAIN, 15th century

*Écu de Saint Pierre of Philip the Good*

Gold Coin, Diam. 1-1/16 inches (2.7 cm.)

EXHIBITIONS: Detroit Institute of Arts, "The Institute Collects," 1964-1965.

REFERENCES: *The Institute Collects*, Detroit Institute of Arts, 1964, p. 22.

Lent by The Detroit Institute of Arts,<br>Gift of Dr. and Mrs. Irving F. Burton

136  FRANCE, late 14th century

*Compte de la vennerie de Charles VI pour l'année 1395*

Ms. in French: 16 vellum leaves, H. 13-3/4 inches (35.0 cm.), W. 11-13/16 inches (30.0 cm.)

The contents of this ledger convey very well the importance and ceremony attached to hunting amusements at the French royal court around 1400. Recorded in the volume by Philippe de Courgnilleroy, *maistre veneur du roi* of Charles VI are the entire expenses incurred in connection with the chase for the year 1395 until Candelmas, or February 2, 1396.

EX COLLECTION: C. F. G. R. Schwerdt; Sir Thomas Phillipps, Middle Hill, Worcestershire and Thirlestaine House, Cheltenham, ms. 4365; [E. P. Goldschmidt]; David Wagstaff.

REFERENCES: W. H. Bond and C. U. Faye, Supplement to the *Census of Medieval and Renaissance Manuscripts in the United States and Canada*, New York, 1962, p. 28, no. 94.

Lent by Yale University Library,
Gift of Mrs. David Wagstaff, 1946

137  PARIS, December 12, 1407

*Proclamation against Outlawry: Letters Patent of Charles VI, King of France, countersigned De La Teillaye*

Ms. in French: 1 vellum sheet written in bâtarde script, H. 15-1/2 inches (39.3 cm.), W. 22-3/8 inches (56.8 cm.)

This historical document which was issued by Charles VI as an ordinance against the assembly of people for making war against the French crown, and outlawing the pillaging that was widespread in the kingdom of France at the time, reflects the deplorable state of affairs in France and the concern of the unhappy and trouble-ridden monarch Charles VI.

The war with England was to be renewed, and over the next decade Charles would have to help the Burgundians in their war against the Armagnacs; but these problems must have seemed remote from the troubles that ensued much sooner. Less than three months after Charles had issued this proclamation he had on his hands a murderer in the person of John the Fearless, Duke of Burgundy, who had slain the Duke of Orléans, confessed his deed, and then publicly denied feeling any moral responsibility because, as he explained, he had not openly defied any warning from the King.

REFERENCES: Unidentified catalogue (description acquired with the original); De Ricci and Wilson, *Census*, II, p. 1541.

Lent by The Pierpont Morgan Library, New York

138  POISSY, April 25 [1492]

*Letter signed Charles VIII, King of France, countersigned Bohier, to Piero de' Medici*

Ms. in French: Paper sheet written in bâtarde script, H. 9-3/8 inches (23.2 cm.), W. 8 inches (20.3 cm.)

It has been discovered only recently that this letter described by De Ricci as "asking him [Piero de' Medici] to send two musicians" concerns not just any two performers, but a pair of musicians one of whom was a major musical figure in European circles at the end of the fifteenth and beginning of the sixteenth centuries. Martin Picker was the first to rediscover that Alexander Agricola, often referred to with praise by the poet Jean Lemaire de Belges, is mentioned specifically in this letter. As the document reveals, Agricola, who some years earlier had been at the court of the Duke of Milan together with Josquin des Préz and other illustrious musicians of his time, and later was patronized by

Lorenzo de' Medici as a singer at Florence Cathedral, was also, still later, in the employ of Charles VIII.

In essence, in this letter Charles tells Piero, son of the lately deceased Lorenzo the Magnificent, that he wishes to have Agricola, "singer of our chapel," returned to him, and explains to his "dear and beloved cousin": "because we particularly desire the return to our chapel of this Alexander, we are writing to him immediately directing that he come before us and that he bring with him the said lutinest." Sometime before April, 1492, and without leave, Agricola had departed for Florence with his lutinest friend. As Mr. Picker has pointed out, it is known from other sources that he probably left Florence in June of that year. Whether or not he complied with Charles' wish and returned to France is not known for certain, but Picker discovers stylistic elements in his later music that suggest renewed contact at that time with Johannes Ockeghem, Charles' chapel-master (d. ca. 1495).

EX COLLECTION: G A R (unidentified collector's mark); Julian Marshall.

REFERENCES: J. R. Sterndale-Bennett, in *Grove's Dictionary of Music and Musicians,* London, I, 1879, p. 44; De Ricci and Wilson, *Census,* II, no. 1542; Martin Picker, in *Aspects of Medieval and Renaissance Music. A Birthday Offering to Gustave Reis,* edited by Jan La Rue, New York, 1966, pp. 665-672.

Lent by The Pierpont Morgan Library, New York

PLATE IV

No. 80

No. 78

No. 82

PLATE III

No. 42

No. 2

No. 2

PLATE II

PLATE I

PLATE V

No. 81

No. 84

No. 79

PLATE VI

No. 96

PLATE VII

No. 93

No. 92

PLATE VIII

No. 44

No. 83

PLATE IX

PLATE X

PLATE XI

No. 45

PLATE XII

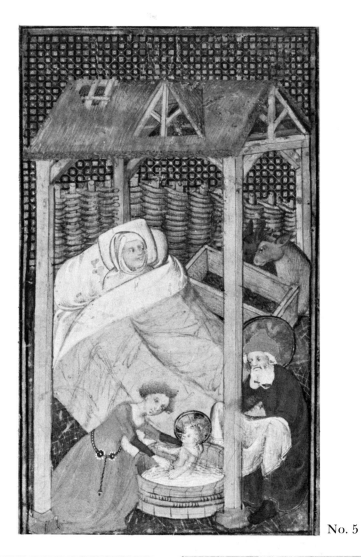

No. 5

No. 6

No. 94

PLATE XIII

PLATE XIV

No. 47

No. 47

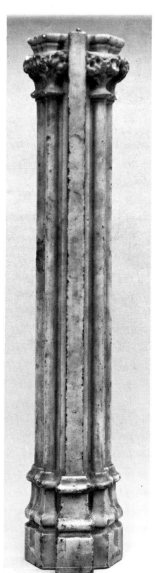

No. 47

PLATE XV

No. 46

No. 97

No. 48

PLATE XVI

No. 8

No. 7

No. 7

PLATE XX

No. 53

PLATE XIX

No. 86

No. 86

PLATE XVIII

No. 87

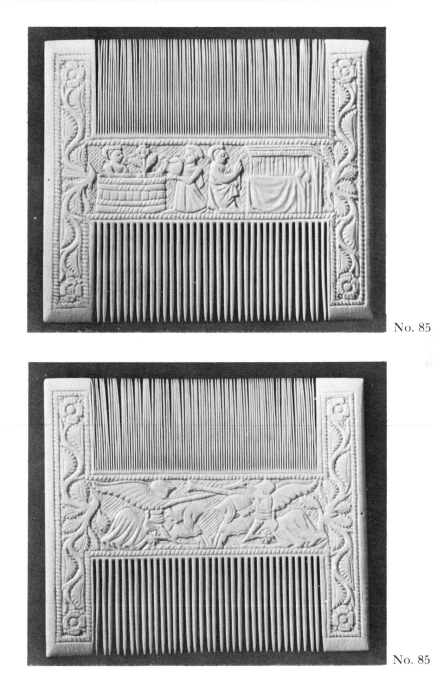

No. 85

No. 85

PLATE XVII

No. 122

PLATE XXI

No. 52

No. 54

No. 55

PLATE XXII

No. 49

PLATE XXIII

No. 50

PLATE XXIV

No. 56

No. 32

PLATE XXV

No. 100

PLATE XXVI

No. 123

No. 124

PLATE XXVII

PLATE XXVIII

PLATE XXIX

PLATE XXX

¶ Y commence la Premiere partie de ce liure laquelle parle du Fente de
qui est contre les sept pechez mortelz · Et premierement · Comment
Orgueil desplaist a dieu · de quoy parle ce premier Chapitre ·

ous orgueilleux
se veulent adieu
comparer en tant
quilz se glorifiet
en eulx mesmes et es biens quilz
ont ¶ Desquelles choses la gloire
est deue principalement adieu ·
¶ Et est grant abusion quant
creature prent orgueil en soy mes
mes pour les biens que dieu lui
enuoye pour lesquelz elle deuoit
estre plus humble enuers dieu et
meulx se recognoistre et le seruir

plus deuotement pour tant dist
le prophete que dieu resiste aux
orgueilleux lesquelz sont cheuz
villainement entre lesquelz
fut premier lucifer · lequel par
son orgueil cheut de paradis en
enfer lui et tous ceulx qui consen
tirent a leur peche ¶ Semblable
ment nostre premier pere adam
par sa mesprison desobeist a dieu
et obeist au serpent disant quil
seroit comme dieu mais quil me
geast du fruit qui lui estoit deffedu

PLATE XXXI

No. 10

No. 11

PLATE XXXII

PLATE XXXIII

No. 35

No. 35

PLATE XXXIV

PLATE XXXV

No. 21

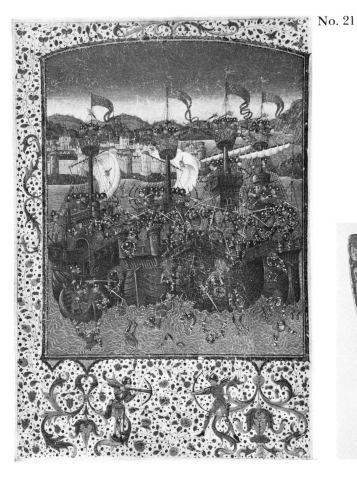

No. 109

No. 39

PLATE XXXVI

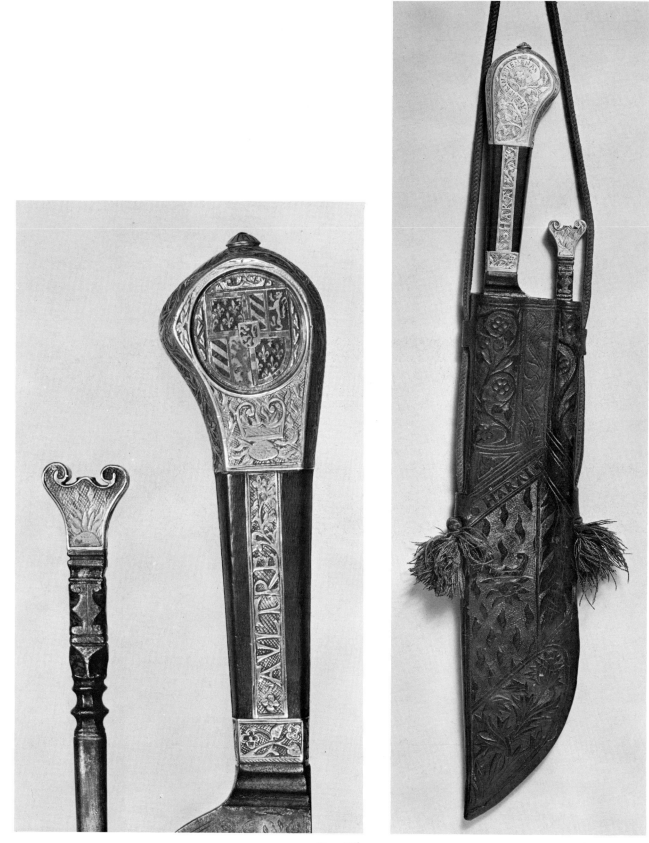

No. 103

No. 103

PLATE XXXVII

Le prologue du translateur des commentaires de Julle cesar.

Res hault
Tres puissāt
tres excellent
victorieux et
xpresticū pn̄
ce Mon tres
redoubte seigneur Charles
par la grace d̄ dieu Duc de
bourgoigne · de locrick · de brabāt

de lembourg Et de luxembourg
Conte de flandres · dartois ·
de bourgoigne · Palatin de he
nau · d̄ hollande · d̄ zeelande
et d̄ namur · marquis du saint
empire Seigneur de frise · de
salins et de malines et c̄·
Pour ce que au commencemēt
d̄ toutes choses contendue

PLATE XXXVIII

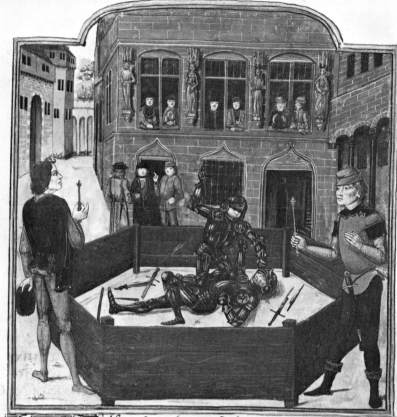

reshault tres
excellent et
tresscenstre
seigneur
Richard par la grace de
dieu Roy dangleterre z
seigneur delande Tho
mas duc de closestre vre
connestable dangleterre
honneur z toute obeissace
Comme pluss bataillez

dedens litez armez ayent
este faittez en vostre roy
aume ou tempz de mos
z pere vostre ayeul come
en vostre tempz z de preset
plus que ne furent long
tempz deuant z que bien
est apparant de plus en
auoir. Et pour ce que a
vostre tsexcellente royale
maieste en appartient la

PLATE XXXIX

No. 23

PLATE XL

F V·B

PLATE XLI

No. 127

PLATE XLII

No. 13

No. 12

PLATE XLIII

Et quant le duc ur ur houuel raur Et comanda git tristence

quite deuorent Aldonc leisse
rent contre lee theuaulr de grant
randon et sentu fenieu delance
qui moult estorent fors et roide
et lee bassaulz estorent tone y
fore et puissant et bone thliere
et sentaenontrerent si tres roide
ment que lee lances froicreent
Insignce aux punesse et sente
fierrerent de corpt et de heaul
mce si fort que lee theuaulr
chairent mors en laplace et fu
rent lee heaulmes tous enbar
rce et furent lee theualiere se
estonidie que lun chaidnne pt
et lautre dautre maue artue ch

fut le plus bertueur sailli tautost
sur lee piez et mist la main a
son espee trenche fez et son com
paumon chefou en corde lee piez
contre mont et lateste aual Et
quant artue but quil chesoit a
malaise si lui tourna lateste
contre mont et lui mist son estu
dessoubz et puie se trai arriere
Dont il fut moult prise du Roy
et detoute labaronie et diff le
Roy axble moult a ce theualier
lecuer chentil et noble certes
il ne puet estre quil ne soit de
bon lieu Et quant le nepueu
du duc fut venenu si sailli sus

PLATE XLIV

No. 102

No. 101

PLATE XLV

No. 99

No. 108

PLATE XLVI

PLATE XLVII

No. 30

PLATE XLVIII

No. 64

No. 63

PLATE XLIX

No. 28

No. 29

PLATE L

No. 125

PLATE LI

No. 15

No. 17

PLATE LII

No. 9

No. 15

No. 57

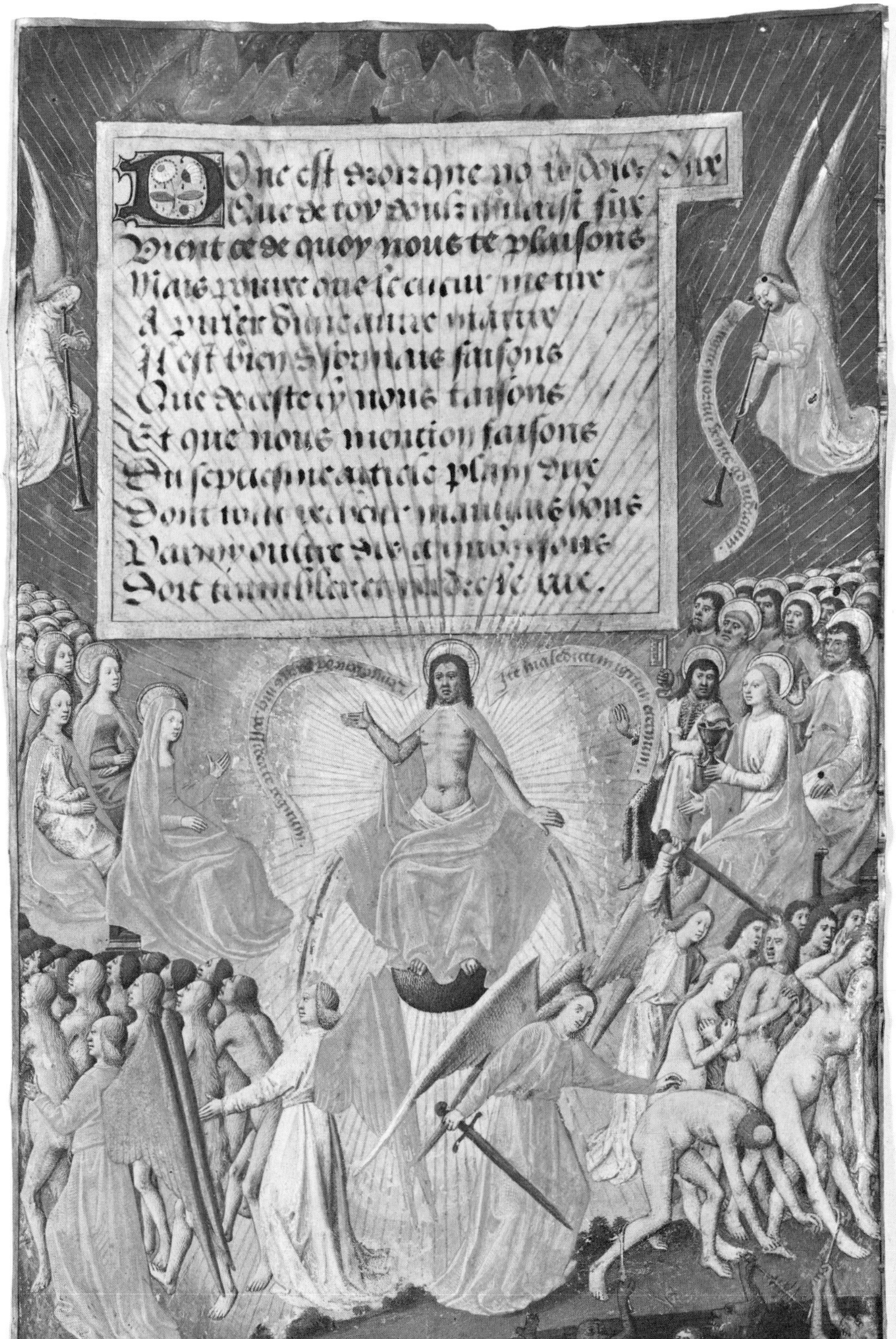

No. 14

PLATE LIV

No. 62

No. 98

PLATE LV

No. 58

Nos. 59, 60

PLATE LVI

No. 61

No. 16

PLATE LVII

No. 16

No. 115

PLATE LVIII

No. 24

No. 105

No. 91

PLATE LIX

No. 68

No. 25

PLATE LX

No. 66

PLATE LXI

No. 65

No. 67

PLATE LXII

No. 70

No. 89

PLATE LXIII

No. 69

No. 72

PLATE LXIV

No. 73

No. 119

PLATE LXV

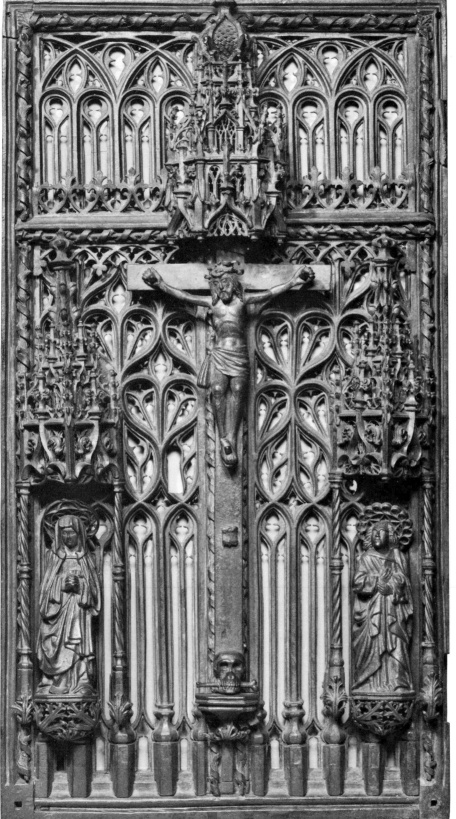

No. 120

PLATE LXVI

No. 75

No. 118

PLATE LXVII

No. 76

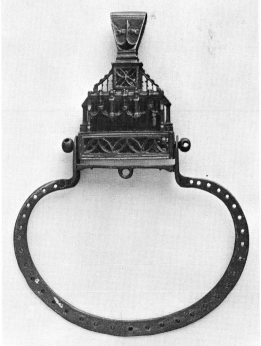

No. 116

PLATE LXVIII

No. 38

No. 106                    No. 107

PLATE LXIX

PLATE LXX

PLATE LXXI

No. 128

PLATE LXXII

No. 71

No. 88

PLATE LXXIII

No. 130

No. 117

PLATE LXXIV

No. 126

PLATE LXXV

No. 132

No. 37

PLATE LXXVI

No. 133